CARNEGIE LEARNING
LONG + LIVE + MATH

Middle School Math Solution
Course 1

Student Edition
Volume 2

Sandy Bartle Finocchi and Amy Jones Lewis

with Kelly Edenfield and Josh Fisher

CARNEGIE LEARNING

501 Grant St., Suite 1075
Pittsburgh, PA 15219
Phone 888.851.7094
Customer Service Phone 412.690.2444
Fax 412.690.2444

www.carnegielearning.com

Cover Design by Anne Milliron

ISBN: 978-1-68459-285-2
Student Edition, Volume 2

Printed in the United States of America
2 3 4 5 6 7 8 9 BB 21 20 21

LONG + LIVE + MATH

Acknowledgments

Middle School Math Solution Authors
- Sandy Bartle Finocchi, Senior Academic Officer
- Amy Jones Lewis, Director of Instructional Design
- Kelly Edenfield, Instructional Designer
- Josh Fisher, Instructional Designer

Foundation Authors (2010)
- William S. Hadley, Algebra and Proportional Reasoning
- Mary Lou Metz, Data Analysis and Probability
- Mary Lynn Raith, Number and Operations
- Janet Sinopoli, Algebra
- Jaclyn Snyder, Geometry and Measurement

Vendors
- Lumina Datamatics, Ltd.
- Cenveo Publisher Services, Inc.

Images
- www.pixabay.com

Special Thanks
- Alison Huettner for project management and editorial review.
- Jacyln Snyder and Janet Sinopoli for their contributions to the Teacher's Implementation Guide facilitation notes.
- Victoria Fisher for her review of content and contributions to all the ancillary materials.
- Valerie Muller for her contributions and review of content.
- The members of Carnegie Learning's Cognitive Scientist Team—Brendon Towle, John Connelly, Bob Hausmann, Chas Murray, and Martina Pavelko—for their insight in learning science and review of content.
- Bob Hausmann for his contributions to the Family Guide.
- John Jorgenson, Chief Marketing Officer, for all his insight and messaging.
- Carnegie Learning's Education Services Team for content review and providing customer feedback.
- In Memory of David Dengler, Director of Curriculum Development (Deceased), who made substantial contributions to conceptualizing Carnegie Learning's middle school software.

"Mathematics is so much more than memorizing rules. It is learning to reason, to make connections, and to make sense of the world. We believe in Learning by Doing(TM)—you need to actively engage with the content if you are to benefit from it. The lessons were designed to take you from your intuitive understanding of the world and build on your prior experiences to then learn new concepts. My hope is that these instructional materials help you build a deep understanding of math."

Sandy Bartle Finocchi, Senior Academic Officer

"My hope is that as you work through this course, you feel capable—capable of exploring new ideas that build upon what you already know, capable of struggling through challenging problems, capable of thinking creatively about how to fix mistakes, and capable of thinking like a mathematician."

Amy Jones Lewis, Director of Instructional Design

"At Carnegie Learning we have created an organization whose mission and culture is defined by your success. Our passion is creating products that make sense of the world of mathematics and ignite a passion in you. Our hope is that you will enjoy our resources as much as we enjoyed creating them."

Barry Malkin, CEO

Table of Contents

Module 1: Composing and Decomposing

Module 2: Relating Quantities

Topic 1: Ratios

Topic 2: Percents

Topic 3: Unit Rates and Conversions

Module 3: Determining Unknown Quantities

Module 4: Moving Beyond Positive Quantities

Module 5: Describing Variability of Quantities

DETERMINING UNKNOWN
QUANTITIES

The lessons in this module build on your knowledge of numeric expressions, patterns, and operations, which you developed throughout elementary school. You will use properties of arithmetic and apply them to algebraic expressions. You will investigate equations and graphs and develop strategies to make sense of and reason about unknown quantities in real-world and mathematical problems.

TOPIC 1
Expressions

Emojis in emails and chat messages show different expressions. Mathematical expressions are a little different. But you probably already knew that. ☺

Module 3: Determining Unknown Quantities

TOPIC 1: EXPRESSIONS

In this topic, students develop their understanding of variables and algebraic expressions. They also formalize their knowledge of powers and evaluate expressions involving whole number exponents, expanding their application of the Order of Operations to include exponents. Students compose algebraic expressions from verbal statements, decompose expressions into their component terms, and evaluate algebraic expressions for given values of the variable. They use algebra tiles and properties of arithmetic and algebra to form equivalent expressions, just as they did in previous lessons with numeric expressions. Students also use tables and graphs to determine if expressions are equivalent, and they write algebraic expressions to model and solve real-world and mathematical problems.

Where have we been?

Students enter grade 6 with knowledge of factors and properties of numbers. They have used the Commutative and Associative Properties in first and third grades and the Order of Operations, although formal terminology may not have been used. These properties, along with the Distributive Property, were reviewed in previous lessons in this course. During elementary school, students wrote expressions with whole number exponents for powers of ten, and they wrote numeric expressions to record verbal descriptions of calculations.

Where are we going?

This topic provides the foundation for future work with algebraic structures, including algebraic equations and inequalities and their representations. Expressions are the foundation of equations. Expertise in writing expressions enables students to write and solve equations for many real-world and mathematical problems. As students continue in the course, they must be able to evaluate expressions and determine whether expressions are equivalent.

Using Algebra Tiles to Model Expressions

Algebra tiles are used to model expressions with variables. For example, this model could show the combination of the expressions $x + 1$ and $2x + 1$. The sum can be written, even when the value of x is not known. The model shows that the sum is $3x + 2$.

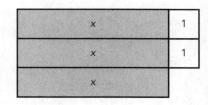

Myth: "I learn best when the instruction matches my learning style."

If asked, some people will tell you they have a *learning style* – the expressed preference in learning by seeing images, hearing speech, seeing words, or being able to physically interact with the material. Some people even believe that it is the teacher's job to present the information in accordance with that preference.

However, it turns out that the best scientific evidence available does not support learning styles. In other words, when an auditory learner receives instruction about content through a visual model, they do just as well as auditory learners who receive spoken information. Students may have a *preference* for visuals or writing or sound, but sticking to their preference doesn't help them learn any better. Far more important is ensuring the student is engaged in an interactive learning activity and the new information connects to the student's prior knowledge.

#mathmythbusted

Talking Points

You can support your student's learning by resisting the urge, as long as possible, to get to the answer in a problem that your student is working on. Students will learn the algebraic shortcuts that you may know about, but only once they have experience in mathematical reasoning. This may seem to take too long at first. But if you practice asking good questions instead of helping your student arrive at the answer, they will learn to rely on their own knowledge, reasoning, patience, and endurance when struggling with math.

Key Terms

Order of Operations
Evaluate expressions inside parentheses, then exponents, then multiply and divide from left to right, then add and subtract from left to right.

variable
A variable is a symbol, often a letter, that represents a quantity that varies.

algebraic expression
An algebraic expression is a mathematical phrase involving at least one variable, and sometimes numbers and operation symbols.

coefficient
A coefficient is the number that is multiplied by a variable in an algebraic expression.

Relationships Matter

Evaluating Numeric Expressions

WARM UP

Write each power of ten as a product of factors. Then calculate the product.

1. $10^2 = $ _____ = _____

2. $10^5 = $ _____ = _____

3. $10^3 = $ _____ = _____

4. $10^4 = $ _____ = _____

5. $10^7 = $ _____ = _____

LEARNING GOALS

- Interpret a number raised to a positive integer power as a repeated product.
- Identify perfect square numbers and perfect cube numbers.
- Write and evaluate numeric expressions involving whole-number exponents.
- Model numeric expressions with two- and three-dimensional figures.
- Evaluate numeric expressions using the Order of Operations.

KEY TERMS

- power
- base
- exponent
- perfect square
- perfect cube
- evaluate a numeric expression
- Order of Operations

You have written and evaluated expressions equivalent to given numbers. Besides the four operations—addition, subtraction, multiplication, and division—are there other structures that can be used in numeric expressions?

Expression Challenge

Recall that an expression in mathematics is a number or a combination of numbers and operations. The number 8 is an expression, and $2 \times 2 + 4$ is also an expression. Both of these expressions are equal to 8.

1. Write an expression that is equal to 10 using only four 2s and any number of math symbols.

Is there more than one way to write each expression?

2. Write an expression that is equal to 8 using only four 3s and any number of math symbols.

3. Write an expression that is equal to 20 using only one 2 and two 4s and any number of math symbols.

Square and Cube Numbers

Just as repeated addition can be represented as a multiplication problem, repeated multiplication can be represented as a *power*. A **power** has two elements: the base and the exponent.

$$2 \times 2 \times 2 \times 2 = 2^4$$

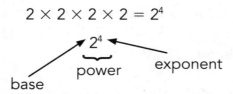

The **base** of a power is the factor that is multiplied repeatedly in the power, and the **exponent** of the power is the number of times the base is used as a factor.

> You can read a power in different ways:
> "2 to the fourth power"
> "2 raised to the fourth power"

1. **Identify the base and exponent in each power. Then, write each power in words.**

   a. 7^5 b. 4^8

Remember that the area of a rectangle is calculated by multiplying its length by its width. Because all sides of a square have the same length, the area of a square, A, is calculated by multiplying the length of the side, s, by itself. The formula for the area of a square, $A = s \times s$, can be written as $A = s^2$.

> In the power s^2, the base is the side length, s, and the exponent is 2.

In the same way, to calculate the square of a number, you multiply the number by itself.

2. **Write the area of each square as a repeated product, as a square number, and as an area in square units.**

   a.

   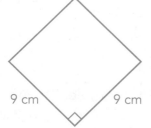

   9 cm   9 cm

   b.

   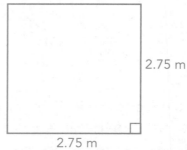

   2.75 m

   2.75 m

c.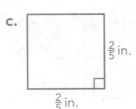

$\frac{2}{5}$ in.

$\frac{2}{5}$ in.

d.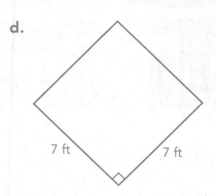

7 ft   7 ft

You can read 3^2 as "3 squared."

Some of the areas that you wrote in Question 1 are called **perfect squares** because they are squares of an integer. For example, 9 is a perfect square because $3 \times 3 = 9$. Another way you can write this mathematical sentence is $3^2 = 9$.

In the power s^3, the base is the side length, s, and the exponent is 3.

Recall that the volume of a cube is calculated by multiplying its length by its width and its height. Since the length, width, and height of a cube are all the same, the formula for the volume, V, of a cube can be written as $V = s \times s \times s$, or $V = s^3$.

In the same way, to calculate the cube of a number, you use the number as a factor three times.

3. **Write the volume of each cube as a repeated product, as the cube of a number, and as a volume in cubic units.**

a.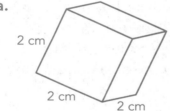

2 cm

2 cm

2 cm

b.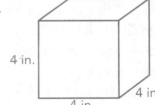

4 in.

4 in.

4 in.

c.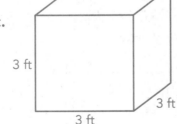

3 ft

3 ft

3 ft

d.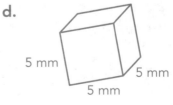

5 mm

5 mm

5 mm

You can read 6^3 as "6 cubed."

A **perfect cube** is the cube of an integer. For example, 216 is a perfect cube because 6 is a whole number and $6 \times 6 \times 6 = 216$.

Modeling Expressions

Previously, you may have thought about expressions as recipes. For example, the expression 2 + 2 might have meant "start with 2 and add 2 more." But as a relationship, 2 + 2 means "2 combined with 2."

The Expression Cards at the end of this lesson contain a variety of numeric expressions and models that represent numeric expressions. Cut out the Expression Cards.

> Remember, a numeric expression is a mathematical phrase that contains numbers and operations.

1. Consider the different structures of the expressions and the models.

   a. Sort the models in a mathematically meaningful way.
   b. Sort the expressions in a mathematically meaningful way.
   c. Explain how you sorted the Expression Cards.

2. Match the numeric expressions with the models. Select two pairs of cards and explain why each expression matches the model.

Now it's your turn!

3. Think of a numeric expression. Draw a model to represent that expression. Trade your model with a classmate and write the numeric expression that represents their model. When you both have written your answers, trade back and check your work!

The diagram can be used to determine perfect squares.
Daniel drew on the diagram to show that the expression
$(4 + 4)^2$ is equivalent to 8^2.

	1	2	3	4	5	6	7	8	9	10	11	12	13	14	15
1															
2															
3															
4															
5															
6															
7															
8															
9															
10															
11															
12															
13															
14															
15															

Diagonal labels: $1^2 = 1$, $2^2 = 4$, $3^2 = 9$, $4^2 = 16$, $5^2 = 25$, $6^2 = 36$, $7^2 = 49$, $8^2 = 64$, $9^2 = 81$, $10^2 = 100$, $11^2 = 121$, $12^2 = 144$, $13^2 = 169$, $14^2 = 196$, $15^2 = 225$

How can you
use the grid
to determine
the square of
any number
from 1 to 15?

1. Explain why $(4 + 4)^2$ is equivalent to 8^2 and not equivalent to
   $4^2 + 4^2$. Then use the diagram to write other expressions that
   are equivalent to 8^2.

2. Write an equivalent numeric expression for each perfect square.

   a. 6^2

   b. 12^2

To **evaluate a numeric expression** means to simplify the expression to a single numeric value.

3. Use the diagram to rewrite the expression $(7 - 3)^2 + (10 - 7)^2$ with fewer terms. Explain your work.

4. Use the diagram to write four numeric expressions. Then explain how to evaluate each expression.

The table shows the cubes of the first 10 whole numbers.

$1^3 = 1$	$2^3 = 8$	$3^3 = 27$	$4^3 = 64$	$5^3 = 125$
$6^3 = 216$	$7^3 = 343$	$8^3 = 512$	$9^3 = 729$	$10^3 = 1000$

5. Write two more equivalent expressions for each. Show how to evaluate the expressions.

   a. 5^3

   b. 2^3

ACTIVITY
1.4 Evaluating Expressions

Consider the numeric expression $2 \cdot 5^2$.

1. **Shae drew a model to represent the expression. Explain how Shae's model represents the expression. Then evaluate the expression.**

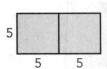

2. **Doug and Miguel each evaluated the expression differently.**

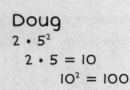

Miguel
$2 \cdot 5^2$
$5^2 = 25$
$2 \cdot 25 = 50$

Doug
$2 \cdot 5^2$
$2 \cdot 5 = 10$
$10^2 = 100$

a. **What does Miguel's solution tell you about how to evaluate a numeric expression with both multiplication and exponents?**

b. **Draw a model to represent Doug's solution. Explain how the model is different from Shae's.**

Parentheses are symbols used to group numbers and operations. You can think about expressions inside parentheses as a single value.

3. **This model represents the expression $(6 + 4) \cdot 3$.**

a. **Evaluate the expression represented by the model.**

6	4
6	4
6	4

b. Draw a model that would represent the expression
   6 + (4 · 3) and evaluate the expression.

c. Compare the models and the expressions. How does
   moving the parentheses change how you draw the model
   and how you evaluate the expression?

4. Consider the numeric expression $(5 + 3)^2$.

   a. Draw a model to represent this expression.

   b. The numeric expression was evaluated in two different
      ways, resulting in two different values. Determine which
      solution is correct. Explain why one solution is correct and
      state the error that was made in the other solution.

Solution A	Solution B
$(5 + 3)^2$	$(5 + 3)^2$
$= 8^2$	$= 25 + 9$
$= 64$	$= 34$

5. Consider the numeric expression $3 · (7 - 2)$.

   a. Draw a model to represent this expression.

   b. The numeric expression was evaluated in two different
      ways, resulting in two different values. Determine which
      solution is correct. Explain why one solution is correct and
      state the error that was made in the other solution. Cross
      out the incorrect solution.

Solution A	Solution B
$3 · (7 - 2)$	$3 · (7 - 2)$
$= 21 - 2$	$= 3(5)$
$= 19$	$= 15$

6. A band is playing at a local restaurant for a total of 8 Fridays and will be paid after their last performance. The band advertises their 8 appearances in the local newspaper for a total cost of $400. If the band makes $500 for each appearance, which numeric expression correctly shows the amount of money each of the four members will earn? Explain your reasoning.

Expression A
$(8 \cdot 500 - 400) \div 4$

Expression B
$8 \cdot 500 - 400 \div 4$

ACTIVITY **1.5**	**The Order of Operations**

We can use "Please Excuse My Dear Aunt Sally" to remember Parentheses, Exponents, Multiplication and Division, and Addition and Subtraction, right?

There is an *Order of Operations,* an order in which operations are performed when evaluating any numeric expression. The **Order of Operations** is a set of rules that ensures the same result every time an expression is evaluated.

Order of Operations Rules

1. Evaluate expressions inside parentheses or grouping symbols.
2. Evaluate exponents.
3. Multiply and divide from left to right.
4. Add and subtract from left to right.

Keep in mind that multiplication and division are of equal importance and evaluated in order from left to right. The same is true for addition and subtraction.

I like "Pink Elephants Must Dance Around Snakes" better. Is that OK?

A mnemonic may help you remember the order. The important thing is to understand WHY the order of operations works.

Evaluate each expression using the Order of Operations.

1. $28 \div 2^2 - 36 \div 3^2$

2. $12 + (25 \div 5)^2$

3. $(12^2 - 48) \times 2$

4. $168 \div 2^3 + 3^3 - 20$

5. $10 \div (5 - 3) + 2^3$

TALK the TALK

Order of Operations

Determine whether or not each expression was evaluated correctly. Show the correct work for any incorrect answers.

1. $18 \div 2 \cdot 3^2$
    $18 \div 2 \cdot 9$
    $18 \div 18$
    1

2. $(15 + 10 \div 5) + 8$
    $(15 + 2) + 8$
    $17 + 8$
    25

3. $60 - (10 - 6 + 1)^2 \cdot 2$
    $60 - (10 - 7)^2 \cdot 2$
    $60 - (3)^2 \cdot 2$
    $60 - 9 \cdot 2$
    $60 - 18$
    42

Each numeric expression has been evaluated correctly and incorrectly. For those that have been evaluated correctly, state how the Order of Operations was used to evaluate the expression. For those expressions that have been evaluated incorrectly, determine the error that was made.

4. $2(10 - 1) - 3 \cdot 2$
    $2(9) - 3 \cdot 2$
    $18 - 3 \cdot 2$
    $15 \cdot 2$
    30

    $2(10 - 1) - 3 \cdot 2$
    $2(9) - 3 \cdot 2$
    $18 - 6$
    12

5. $4 + 3^2$
    $4 + 9$
    13

    $4 + 3^2$
    7^2
    49

6. $(2 + 6)^2$
    8^2
    64

    $(2 + 6)^2$
    $4 + 36$
    40

Expression Cards

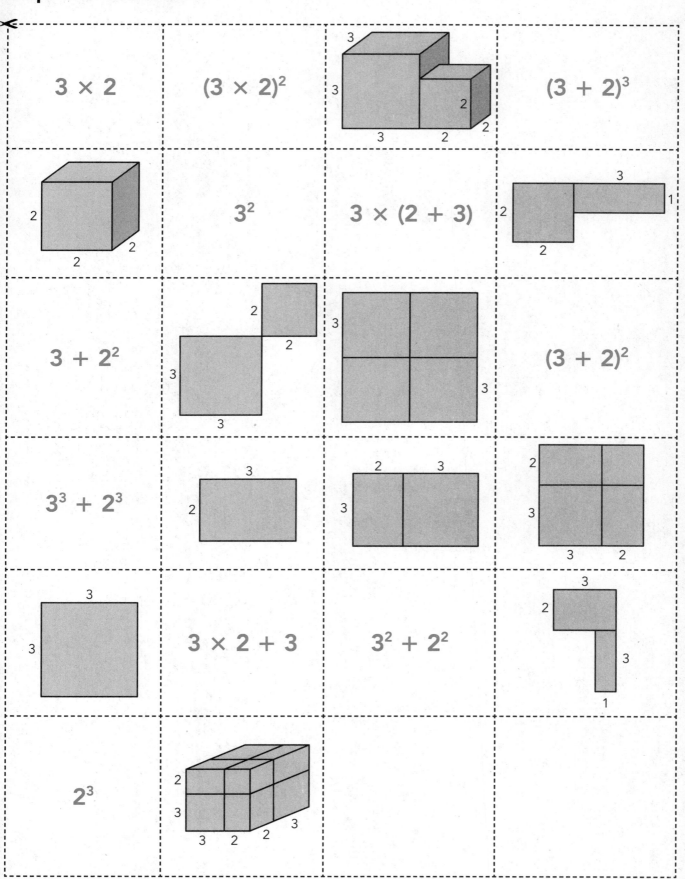

3×2

$(3 \times 2)^2$

$(3 + 2)^3$

3^2

$3 \times (2 + 3)$

$3 + 2^2$

$(3 + 2)^2$

$3^3 + 2^3$

$3 \times 2 + 3$

$3^2 + 2^2$

2^3

Assignment

Write

Write your own mnemonic for the Order of Operations.

Remember

Memorize the first 15 squares and 10 cubes.

Perfect Squares				
$1^2 = 1$	$2^2 = 4$	$3^2 = 9$	$4^2 = 16$	$5^2 = 25$
$6^2 = 36$	$7^2 = 49$	$8^2 = 64$	$9^2 = 81$	$10^2 = 100$
$11^2 = 121$	$12^2 = 144$	$13^2 = 169$	$14^2 = 196$	$15^2 = 225$
Perfect Cubes				
$1^3 = 1$	$2^3 = 8$	$3^3 = 27$	$4^3 = 64$	$5^3 = 125$
$6^3 = 216$	$7^3 = 343$	$8^3 = 512$	$9^3 = 729$	$10^3 = 1000$

Practice

Use the Order of Operations to evaluate each numeric expression.

1. $4^2 \cdot 3$
2. $3^3 - 14 \div 2 + 5$
3. $17 - 2^3$
4. $144 \div 6^2 \cdot 8 + 2^2$
5. $32 \div 4^2$
6. $2^4 - 3 \cdot 5 + 9$
7. $9 + 5^2 - 2 \cdot 3^2$
8. $11^2 - 7 \cdot 6 - 4^3 \div 2$

Stretch

Evaluate each power raised to a power.

1. $(3^2)^2$
2. $(5^2)^4$
3. $(4^3)^2$

Review

Graph each rate in the given pair on a coordinate plane. Explain whether or not the rates are equivalent.

1. $\dfrac{15 \text{ cups flour}}{8.25 \text{ cups sugar}}, \dfrac{5 \text{ cups flour}}{2.75 \text{ cups sugar}}$

2. $\dfrac{245 \text{ mi}}{3.5 \text{ h}}, \dfrac{150 \text{ mi}}{2 \text{ h}}$

Calculate each conversion.

3. 4 grams = _____ milligrams

4. 6400 ounces = _____ pounds

Determine each sum.

5. $\dfrac{6}{7} + 3\dfrac{1}{5}$

6. $1\dfrac{2}{3} + 4\dfrac{1}{4}$

Into the Unknown

Introduction to Algebraic Expressions

WARM UP

In the school cafeteria, soft pretzels sell for $1.25 each. Determine how much money the cafeteria earns in each situation.

1. On Monday, the cafeteria sold 14 soft pretzels.

2. On Wednesday, the cafeteria sold 35 soft pretzels.

3. On Thursday, the cafeteria sold 50 soft pretzels.

LEARNING GOALS

- Write algebraic expressions to represent real-world and mathematical situations.
- Match algebraic and verbal expressions.
- Identify parts of an algebraic expression using mathematical terms.
- Evaluate algebraic expressions at specific values of their variables.

KEY TERMS

- variable
- algebraic expression
- coefficient
- term
- evaluate an algebraic expression

You have written and evaluated expressions made up of numbers, but often expressions are made up of numbers and letters. What situations can be represented by expressions with letters and how do you evaluate them?

Do You Speak Math?

Rewrite each statement using symbols.

1. fourteen more than six

2. six more than fourteen

3. seven less than thirteen

4. thirteen less than seven

5. twenty-three subtracted from thirty

6. thirty subtracted from twenty-three

7. the quotient of twelve divided by four

8. the quotient of four divided by twelve

9. one-fourth of twenty-eight

10. two to the seventh power

11. seven squared

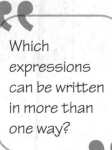

Which expressions can be written in more than one way?

Writing Expressions with Variables

Consider the quantity that changes as you think about the situations in Question 1.

1. A school lunch costs $1.85 for each student. For each situation, write a numeric expression to determine how much money is collected. Then evaluate the expression.

   a. Fifty-five students purchase a school lunch.

   b. One hundred twenty-six students purchase a school lunch.

   c. Two hundred thirteen students purchase a school lunch.

   d. One thousand five hundred twelve students purchase a school lunch.

2. Write a sentence to describe how you can determine the amount of money collected for any number of students buying school lunches.

In Question 1 there is one quantity that changes or varies—the number of students who bought school lunches. In mathematics, letters are often used to represent quantities that vary. These letters are called **variables**, and they help you write algebraic expressions to represent situations. An **algebraic expression** is an expression that has at least one variable.

3. Write an algebraic expression to represent the total amount of money collected for any number of students buying school lunches.

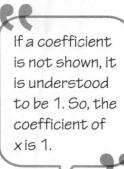

If a coefficient is not shown, it is understood to be 1. So, the coefficient of x is 1.

A number that is multiplied by a variable in an algebraic expression is called a **coefficient**.

4. Identify a coefficient in the expression you wrote in Question 3.

5. The cost to rent a skating rink is $215 for a two-hour party. The cost will be shared equally among all the people who attend the party. For each number of attendees, write a numeric expression to determine how much each person will pay. Then evaluate the expression.

a. 25 attendees

b. 81 attendees

c. 108 attendees

d. Write an algebraic expression to represent how much each person will pay to attend the skate party.

6. Jimmy has three 300-minute international calling cards.

a. Complete the table to determine how many minutes are left on each card after each call.

Minutes on Card	Duration of Call	Minutes Left on Card
300	33 min	
300	57 min	
300	1 h 17 min	

b. Write an algebraic expression that represents the number of minutes remaining after each call on each card.

7. Write an algebraic expression to represent each situation. Identify the coefficient(s).

a. Ben is selling tickets to the school play. How many will he have left if he starts with *t* tickets and sells 125 tickets?

b. A plane descends to $\frac{5}{6}$ of its cruising altitude, *a*. What is its new altitude?

c. A cube has an edge length of *s*.

i. What is the volume of the cube?

ii. What is the surface area of the cube?

d. Used paperback books cost $6.25 each with an additional shipping and handling cost of $8.75. What is the cost of *x* books?

e. Chairs cost $35, and sofas cost $75. How much does it cost to purchase *x* chairs and *y* sofas?

8. Write an algebraic expression to represent each word expression.

a. the quotient of a number *n* divided by 7

b. 5 more than *c*

c. *m* less than 9

d. one-fourth of a number *n*

e. fourteen less than three times a number *n*

f. six times a number *n* subtracted from 21

g. one-fourth of a number *n* minus 6

h. ten times the square of a number *w* divided by 12

ACTIVITY 2.2

Matching Algebraic and Verbal Expressions

Let's play Expression Explosion! You teacher is going to hand out cards. Your goal is to identify the written or algebraic expression that corresponds to your card.

Record your pair of matching algebraic and written expressions.

1. How can you be sure that you have found the correct match?

ACTIVITY 2.3 Parts of Algebraic Expressions

As you learned previously, an algebraic expression contains at least one variable and sometimes numbers and operations. A **term** of an algebraic expression is a number, variable, or product of numbers and variables.

WORKED EXAMPLE

Consider the expression $3x + 4y - 7$.

The expression has three terms: $3x$, $4y$, and 7. The operation between the first two terms is addition, and the operation between the second and third term is subtraction.

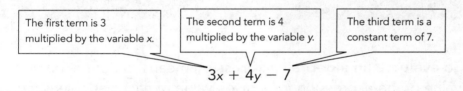

| The first term is 3 multiplied by the variable x. | The second term is 4 multiplied by the variable y. | The third term is a constant term of 7. |

$$3x + 4y - 7$$

1. Consider two algebraic expressions: $8 + 5x$ and $8 - 5x$

   a. Identify the terms in each algebraic expression.

   b. Identify the operation between each term in each algebraic expression.

   c. What is the same in both expressions?

   d. What is different in the expressions?

2. Identify the number of terms, and then the terms themselves for each algebraic expression.

   a. $4 - 3x$

   b. $4a - 9 + 3a$

   c. $7b - 9x + 3a - 12$

Evaluating Algebraic Expressions

To **evaluate an algebraic expression** means to determine the value of the expression for a given value of each variable. When you evaluate an algebraic expression, you substitute the given values for the variables, and then determine the value of the expression.

1. Write a sentence to describe the meaning of each algebraic expression. Then, evaluate the algebraic expression for the given value.

   a. $3x - 4$, for $x = 10$

   b. $11 - s$, for $s = 2$

   c. $10 - z$, for $z = 8$

   d. $5 - \dfrac{y}{4}$, for $y = 2$

Don't forget to use the Order of Operations when evaluating an algebraic expression.

e. $7 + 5a$, for $a = 20$

f. $\frac{b}{4}$, for $b = 8$

2. Complete each table.

a.

h	$3h - 2$
2	
$\frac{7}{3}$	
5.1	
$\frac{5}{6}$	

b.

m	$1 + m$
0	
$\frac{2}{3}$	
4	
1.7	

c.

z	$\frac{2z}{3} + 1$
1	
2	
5	
11	

d.

p	$0.5p$
0	
1	
1.5	
2.5	

TALK the TALK 💬

Expression Construction

1. Construct an algebraic expression for each description.

   a. There are 2 terms. The first term is a constant. It is added to the second term, which is a product of a number and a variable.

   b. There are 4 terms. The first term is a variable divided by 11. This is added to a second term, which is a constant. The third term is a second variable multiplied by three-fourths. The third term is subtracted from the first 2 terms. The last term, a different constant, is added to the other 3 terms.

   c. The cube of a variable subtracted from a constant and then added to the square of the same variable.

   d. A number multiplied by the square of a variable minus a number multiplied by the same variable minus a constant.

It is your turn to challenge your classmates!

2. Create a description for an algebraic expression and swap descriptions with a classmate. After you receive the algebraic expression back from your classmate, answer Question 3.

3. Did your classmate write an expression that fits your description?

Assignment

Write

Complete each statement with the correct term: *algebraic expression, variable, evaluate an algebraic expression, constant, coefficient.*

1. A(n) _____ is a letter used to represent a quantity that varies.

2. A(n) _____ is a number, or quantity, that a variable is multiplied by in an algebraic expression.

3. A number, or quantity, that does not change its value is called a(n) _____.

4. A mathematical phrase involving at least one variable is called a(n) _____.

5. To _____ means to determine the value of the expression.

Remember

Whenever you perform the same mathematical process over and over, you can write a mathematical phrase, called an algebraic expression, to represent the situation.

Practice

Write an algebraic expression to represent each situation.

1. A T-shirt costs $5.99.
   a. How much will you spend if you buy x T-shirts?
   b. Evaluate your expression to calculate the amount of money you will spend if you buy 4 shirts or 10 shirts.

2. You have 7 folders and you want to put the same number of pages in each folder.
   a. If you have a total of p pages, how many pages will be in each folder?
   b. Evaluate your expression to calculate the number of pages in each folder if you have 147 pages or 245 pages.

3. You have a coupon for $5 off your total bill at Mama's Meals on Main.
   a. How much will you pay after using the coupon if your bill was b dollars?
   b. Evaluate your expression to calculate the amount you will pay if your bill was $23.45 or $54.83.

4. You have already read two and a half hours for the Read-a-Thon.
   a. How long will you have read if you read an additional h hours?
   b. Evaluate your expression to calculate the amount of time you will have read if you read 3 or $5\frac{1}{2}$ additional hours.

Write an algebraic expression that represents each verbal expression.

5. six times a number plus 3
6. four times a number subtracted from 2
7. a number squared divided by 2 and added to 16
8. five plus a number and then multiplied by 8

Identify the number of terms and then the terms themselves for each algebraic expression.

9. $6y + 14$
10. $7x - 3y + 12z$
11. $104a + 224b$

Evaluate each algebraic expression for the given value.

12. $34 - y^2$ for $y = 5$
13. $m^3 + 18$ for $m = 2$
14. $\frac{d}{5} + 42$ for $d = 70$

Stretch

Farmer Lyndi raises chickens and goats.

1. Write an expression for the total number of animal legs on Lyndi's farm.
2. How many animal legs are on the farm if Lyndi has 16 chickens and 6 goats?
3. Suppose Lyndi counted 74 animal legs on the farm. How many of each animal might Lyndi have on the farm?

Review

Evaluate each numeric expression.

1. $56 \div 8 + 3 \cdot 6$
2. $9 \cdot 8 - 29 + 30 \div 15 - 15$

Determine which is the better buy.

3. $12.99 for 42 ounces or $2.99 for 10 ounces
4. 3 pounds for $5.00 or $1.50 per pound

Determine at least two equivalent ratios for each given ratio.

5. $\dfrac{2 \text{ eggs}}{5 \text{ cups of milk}}$

6. $\dfrac{20 \text{ red}}{12 \text{ blue}}$

Second Verse, Same as the First

Equivalent Expressions

WARM UP

Evaluate each expression.

1. $5 \div \dfrac{3}{4}$

2. $0.24 \div 0.6$

3. $\dfrac{(14 + 8)}{2}$

4. $\dfrac{14}{2} + \dfrac{8}{2}$

5. What do you notice about the answers to Questions 3 and 4?

LEARNING GOALS

- Model algebraic expressions with algebra tiles.
- Simplify algebraic expressions using algebra tiles.
- Simplify algebraic expressions using the associative, commutative, and distributive properties.
- Apply properties of operations to create equivalent expressions.
- Rewrite expressions as the product of two factors.

KEY TERMS

- like terms
- Distributive Property
- equivalent expressions

You have evaluated numeric expressions and written and evaluated algebraic expressions. How do you combine algebraic expressions, like you did with numeric expressions, into as few terms as possible?

Packing for a Camping Trip

Jaden and Jerome, twin brothers, are packing for a weekend camping trip. They lay out the following items to go in the suitcase.

Jaden: **Jerome:**

1. How many shirts and pairs of pants is each brother packing? Together, how many shirts and pairs of pants are they packing?

	Shirts	Pants
Jaden		
Jerome		
Together		

Your teacher has provided you with algebra tiles.

2. How can you use algebra tiles to model the number of shirts packed by each brother and the number of shirts they packed together?

ACTIVITY
3.1

Algebra Tiles and Combining Like Terms

As you may have seen in the previous activity, when using algebra tiles to model situations and expressions, it is important to have a shared meaning for each differently-sized algebra tile.

Your teacher will hold up each differently-sized algebra tile and tell you the conventional value of each.

1. Sketch each tile and record its value.

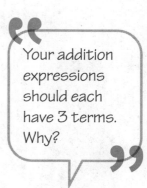

Your addition expressions should each have 3 terms. Why?

2. Represent each numeric or algebraic expression using algebra tiles. Write an addition expression that highlights the different tiles used in the model. Then, sketch the model below the expression.

a. 3

b. 3x

c. $3x^2$

In an algebraic expression, **like terms** are two or more terms that have the same variable raised to the same power. The coefficients of like terms can be different. Let's start our exploration of combining like terms with a review of the properties of arithmetic and algebra that you will use to combine terms.

The expression you wrote in each part of Question 2 was made up of like terms. All tiles that are the same size and have the same value represent like terms.

3. Given the algebra tile model, write an addition expression that highlights the different tiles in the model. Then, if necessary, combine like terms and write the expression using as few terms as possible.

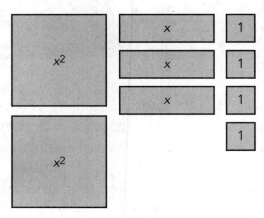

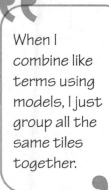

When I combine like terms using models, I just group all the same tiles together.

4. Analyze the last expression you wrote in Question 3.

   a. How many terms are in your expression with the fewest terms? How does this relate to the algebra tile model?

   b. What is the greatest exponent in the expression?

   c. What is the coefficient of x in the expression? How does this relate to your algebra tile model?

5. Consider the model.

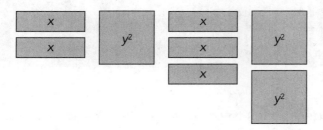

a. Write an addition expression that highlights the different tiles in the model.

b. Rearrange the tiles to combine all of the like tiles. How many terms does your expression have now?

c. Write the new algebraic expression represented.

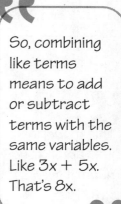

So, combining like terms means to add or subtract terms with the same variables. Like $3x + 5x$. That's $8x$.

6. Represent the algebraic expression $3x^2 + x + 2$ using algebra tiles. How many types of tiles are needed?

Algebra tiles are helpful tools for combining like terms in algebraic expressions. However, because they only represent whole number tiles, they cannot be used to model all algebraic expressions.

7. Use what you have learned about combining like terms to rewrite each algebraic expression with as few terms as possible.

a. $2x + 3x - 4.5x$

b. $3\frac{1}{2}y + 2 + 4y + 1\frac{1}{4}$

c. $4.5x + 6y - 3.5x + 7$

d. $\frac{3}{4}x + 2 + \frac{3}{8}x$

e. $5x + 2y + \frac{1}{3}x^2 - 3x$

ACTIVITY 3.2 — Algebra Tiles and the Distributive Property

When you are speaking about an algebraic expression that is grouped together with parentheses, use the words "the quantity." For example $2(x + 3)$ in words would be "two times the quantity x plus three."

Let's use algebra tiles to explore rewriting algebraic expressions with the Distributive Property.

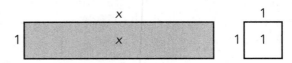

This model is just adding the quantity $x + 1$ five times!

WORKED EXAMPLE

Consider the expression $5(x + 1)$. This expression has two factors: 5 and the quantity $(x + 1)$. You can use the Distributive Property to rewrite this expression. In this case, multiply the 5 by each term of the quantity $(x + 1)$. The model using algebra tiles is shown.

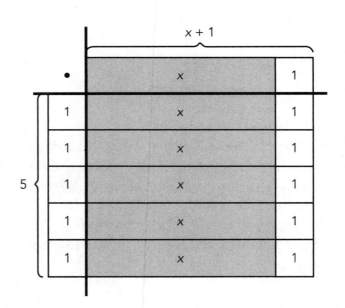

$$5(x + 1) = 5x + 5$$

1. Analyze the parts of the mathematical expressions in the worked example. Explain each response.

   a. Which expression, $5(x + 1)$ or $5x + 5$, shows a product of two factors?

   b. How many terms are in $5x + 5$?

   c. The number 5 is a coefficient in which expression?

2. Create a model of each expression using your algebra tiles. Then, sketch the model and rewrite the expression using the Distributive Property.

   a. $4(2x + 1)$ b. $(3x + 1)2$

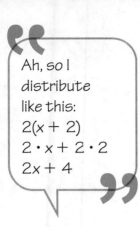

Ah, so I distribute like this:
2(x + 2)
2 · x + 2 · 2
2x + 4

3. Rewrite each expression using the Distributive Property. Then, combine like terms if possible.

a. $2(x + 4)$

b. $\frac{2}{3}(6x + 12)$

c. $2(x + 5) + 4(x + 7)$

d. $5x + 2(3x - 7)$

e. $2(y + 5) + 2(x + 5)$

f. $\frac{1}{2}(4x + 2) + 8x$

So far in this activity, you have multiplied expressions together using the Distributive Property. Now let's think about how to divide expressions.

How do you think the Distributive Property will play a part in dividing expressions? Let's find out.

4. Consider the expression $(4x + 8) \div 4$, which can also be rewritten as $\frac{4x + 8}{4}$.

   a. First, represent $4x + 8$ using your algebra tiles. Sketch the model you create.

   b. Next, divide your algebra tile model into four equal groups. Then, sketch the model you created with your algebra tiles.

   c. Write an expression to represent each group from your sketches in part (b).

   d. Verify you created equal groups by multiplying your expression from part (c) by 4. The product you calculate should equal $4x + 8$.

I know that multiplication and division are inverse operations. So, I should start thinking in reverse.

Let's consider the division expression from Question 4.

To rewrite the
expression, divide
the denominator into
both terms in the
numerator.

WORKED EXAMPLE

You can rewrite an expression of the form $\frac{4x + 8}{4}$ using the Distributive Property.

$$\frac{4x + 8}{4} = \frac{4x}{4} + \frac{8}{4}$$

$$= 1x + 2$$

$$= x + 2$$

So, $\frac{4x + 8}{4} = x + 2$

The model you created in Question 4 is an example that shows that the Distributive Property can be used with division as well as with multiplication.

5. Consider the expression $\frac{2x + 6y + 4}{2}$.

    a. Use algebra tiles to represent the division expression.

    b. Rewrite the division expression using the Distributive Property. Then, simplify the expression.

    $$\frac{2x + 6y + 4}{2} = \frac{2x}{\square} + \frac{6y}{\square} + \frac{4}{\square}$$

    c. Verify that your answer is correct.

    = _____

Zachary thinks he can simplify algebraic expressions that use the Distributive Property with division without using algebra tiles. He wants to rewrite $\dfrac{6 + 3(x + 1)}{3}$ in as few terms as possible and proposes two different methods.

6. Analyze each correct method.

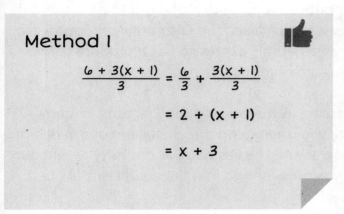
Method 1

$$\frac{6 + 3(x + 1)}{3} = \frac{6}{3} + \frac{3(x + 1)}{3}$$

$$= 2 + (x + 1)$$

$$= x + 3$$

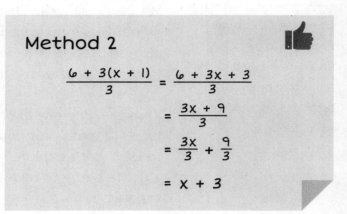
Method 2

$$\frac{6 + 3(x + 1)}{3} = \frac{6 + 3x + 3}{3}$$

$$= \frac{3x + 9}{3}$$

$$= \frac{3x}{3} + \frac{9}{3}$$

$$= x + 3$$

a. Explain the reasoning used in each method.

b. Which method do you prefer. Why?

ACTIVITY 3.3

Factoring Algebraic Expressions

Using the Distributive Property to write an expression as a product of two factors is also known as *factoring*.

You have used the Distributive Property to multiply and divide algebraic expressions by a given value. The Distributive Property can also be used to rewrite an algebraic expression as a product of two factors: a constant and a sum of terms.

You can write any expression as a product of two factors. In many types of math problems, you often need the coefficient of a variable to be 1. Let's explore how to use the Distributive Property — without algebra tiles—to rewrite expressions so that the coefficient of the variable is 1.

1. Consider the expression $3x + 6$.

   a. Identify the coefficient of the variable term.

   b. Use the Distributive Property to rewrite the expression as the product of two factors: the coefficient and a sum of terms.

   c. How can you check your work?

Using the Distributive Property to rewrite the sum of two terms as the product of two factors is also referred to as factoring expressions. In the expression $3x + 6$, you factored out the common factor of 3 from each term and rewrote the expression as $3(x + 2)$. In other words, you divided 3 from each term and wrote the expression as the product of 3 and the sum of the remaining factors, $(x + 2)$.

You can use the same strategy to rewrite an algebraic expression so that the coefficient of the variable is 1 even if the terms do not have common factors.

WORKED EXAMPLE

Let's rewrite the expression $4x - 7$ so the coefficient of the variable is 1.

To rewrite the expression, factor out the coefficient 4 from each term. The equivalent expression is the product of the coefficient and the difference of the remaining factors.

$$4x - 7 = 4\left(\frac{4x}{4} - \frac{7}{4}\right)$$
$$= 4\left(x - \frac{7}{4}\right)$$

Remember, you can multiply or divide any expression by 1 and not change its value.

---

2. Use the Distributive Property to check that the new expression is equivalent to the original expression in the Worked Example.

3. Rewrite each expression as the product of two factors. Check your answers.

   a. $4x + 5$

   b. $8x - 3$

   c. $\frac{1}{2}x - 4$

   d. $1.1x + 1.21$

Rewrite each expression using the Distributive Property.

1. $\dfrac{32 + 4x}{4}$

2. $15x - 10$

3. $\dfrac{3(x + 1) + 12}{3}$

4. $2\dfrac{1}{2} + \dfrac{1}{4}x$

Rewrite each algebraic expression in as few terms as possible.

5. $3x + 5y - 3x + 2y$

6. $4x^2 + 4y + 3x + 2y^2$

7. $7x + 5 - 6x + 2$

8. $x^2 + 5y + 4x^2 - 3y$

Rewrite each algebraic expression by applying the Distributive Property and then combining like terms.

9. $4(x + 5y) - 3x$

10. $2(2x + 5y) + 3(x + 3y)$

11. $3x + 5(2x + 7)$

12. $\dfrac{4x + 6y}{2} - 3y$

13. $3(x + 2y) + \dfrac{3x - 9y}{3}$

14. $2(x + 3y) + 4(x + 5y) - 3x$

TALK the TALK

Write Right

Mr. Martin asked his class to write expressions equivalent to $7(3a + 5b)$ and $8 + 3(2x + 5)$ and got 5 different responses for each. For each response, determine if the original expression was rewritten correctly. For those not rewritten correctly, describe the mistake that was made in rewriting the expression.

1. $7(3a + 5b)$

   a. $10a + 12b$

   b. $7(3a) + 7(5b)$

   c. $21a + 5b$

   d. $21a + 35b$

   e. $7(8ab)$

2. $8 + 3(2x + 5)$

   a. $8 + 3 \cdot 2x + 3 \cdot 5$

   b. $23 + 6x$

   c. $11(2x + 5)$

   d. $8 + 6x + 15$

   e. $13 + 6x$

Assignment

Write

Describe 3 different ways that you can use the Distributive Property to rewrite expressions. Provide an example for each.

Remember

To rewrite an algebraic expression with as few terms as possible, use the properties of arithmetic and the Order of Operations.

An algebraic expression containing terms can be written as the product of two factors by applying the Distributive Property.

Practice

1. Represent each algebraic expression by sketching algebra tiles. Rewrite the expression in a fewer number of terms, if possible.

   a. $x^2 + 2y^2 + 5$

   b. $y^2 + 3y + 1 + y$

2. Rewrite each expression by combining like terms.

   a. $4.5x + (6y - 3.5x) + 7$

   b. $\left(\frac{2}{3}y + \frac{5}{8}x + \frac{1}{4}\right) + \left(\frac{1}{4}x + \frac{1}{2}\right)$

3. Nelson is going on an overnight family reunion camping trip. He is in charge of bringing the wood for the campfire. He will start the fire with 6 logs and then plans to add 3 logs for each hour the fire burns.

   a. Represent the number of logs he will use as an algebraic expression.

   b. Suppose the family decides to stay for 2 nights next year. Write the expression for the number of logs they would need for 2 nights.

   c. Create a model of the situation in part (b) using your algebra tiles, and then sketch the model.

   d. Rewrite the expression in part (c) using as few terms as possible.

   e. Nelson's cousin believes they will only need one-third of the firewood Nelson brings for one night. Represent this as an expression and then use the Distributive Property to rewrite the expression.

   f. There are several family members who will be visiting for the day only. The campground charges $6 per car, plus $2 per visitor. One of the families brings a coupon for $3 off their total fee. Write the expression that represents their total cost for the day. Define the variables.

   g. The two oldest uncles at the reunion insist on paying the bill for the daily visitors. They will split the bill equally. Represent the amount of money each uncle will pay as an expression. Then use the Distributive Property to rewrite the expression.

4. Rewrite each expression by applying the Distributive Property and combining like terms.

   a. $7(2x + y) + 5(x + 4y)$

   b. $9x + 6y + \dfrac{12y + 16x}{4}$

   c. $\dfrac{6(x + 1) + 30}{6}$

5. Rewrite each expression as a product of two factors, so that the coefficient of the variable is 1.

   a. $6x + 7$

   b. $\frac{2}{3}x + 8$

Stretch

1. Simplify the algebraic expression to include as few terms as possible.

   $3[2x + 4(5y + 1)] + \frac{1}{4}\left[8y + 12\left(\frac{2}{3}x + \frac{1}{6}\right)\right]$

2. Rewrite each algebraic expression as the product of two factors, such that the coefficient of the term with the highest exponent is 1.

   a. $2x^2 + 5x + 1$

   b. $\frac{3}{4}x^3 - 9x^2 + \frac{2}{3}x + 10$

   c. $2.6y^2 + 3.9y - 12.48$

Review

1. Sheldon Elementary School has a school store that sells many items including folders, pencils, erasers, and novelty items. The parent association is in charge of buying items for the store.

   a. One popular item at the store is scented pencils that come in packs of 24 from the retailer. Write an algebraic expression that represents the total number of scented pencils they will have available to sell. Let p represent the number of packs of scented pencils.

   b. Another popular item at the store is animal-themed folders. Each pack of folders contains 6 folders. The store currently has 4 packs in the store and would like to order more. Write an algebraic expression for the total number of folders they will have after they order more folders. Let x represent the number of packs of folders they buy.

   c. The latest fad is animal-shaped rubber bracelets. The bracelets come in a pack of 24. Write an algebraic expression that represents the cost of each bracelet. Let c represent the cost of a pack of 24 bracelets.

2. Determine which rate is faster.

   a. 185 miles in 3 hours or 490 miles in 8 hours

   b. 70 miles per hour or 100 kilometers per hour

3. Calculate the volume of each solid formed by rectangular prisms.

   a.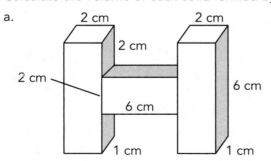
   b.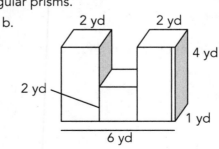

Are They Saying the Same Thing?

Verifying Equivalent Expressions

WARM UP

Determine which pairs of ratios are equivalent. Explain how you know.

1. 5:7 and 100:140

2. 42:48 and 14:15

3. 105:100 and 20:21

4. 9:12 and 60:80

LEARNING GOALS

- Compare expressions using properties, tables, and graphs.
- Identify when two expressions are equivalent.
- Determine if two expressions are equivalent.

You know how to use the Distributive Property and combine like terms to write equivalent expressions. How can you determine if two given expressions are equivalent?

Property Sort

Cut out the Property Cards located at the end of the lesson.

On each card is one representation of a property of numbers or operations that you have used in the past to rewrite and evaluate numeric expressions.

1. **Sort the cards according to the property named or illustrated on the cards. Create a table that shows your final sorting.**

2. **Using complete sentences, write an explanation for how each picture illustrates its property.**

Determining Whether Expressions Are Equivalent

Two algebraic expressions are **equivalent expressions** if, when any values are substituted for the variables, the results are equal.

While it's not realistic to test each expression for every possible value for the unknown, you can examine the characteristics of each expression in the different representations:

- a table of values
- rewritten expressions using the properties
- a graph of both expressions

Let's explore each representation.

Consider the two expressions $2(x + 2) + 3x$ and $5x + 4$.

1. **Use a table to evaluate each expression for different values of the variable.**

   a. **Complete the table of values for each value of x.**

x	$2(x + 2) + 3x$	$5x + 4$
0		
1		
2		
3		

   b. **What can you determine based on the values in the table?**

   c. **What would you need to know to be able to verify that the two expressions are equivalent?**

2. Rewrite the given expression and identify the property applied at each step.

$$2(x + 2) + 3x$$ _____ Given

$$= 2x + \underline{\hspace{1cm}} + 3x$$ _____

$$= \underline{\hspace{1cm}} x + 4$$ _____ Combine Like Terms/Addition

3. Are the two expressions equivalent? Explain.

You can also use a graph to determine or verify if two expressions are equivalent.

4. Use the table of values to sketch the graph of both expressions on the coordinate plane.

a. Plot the values for each expression on the coordinate plane. Use a □ to represent the values from the first expression and a △ for the values from the second expression. Then, connect the results for each expression with a line.

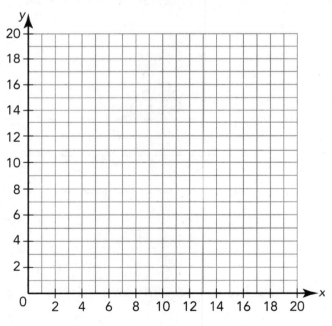

Don't forget to put arrows on each end of your line. The arrows show that the line goes on forever.

b. How does the graph demonstrate that the two expressions are equivalent?

Now, let's consider the expressions $2x + 5$ and $2(x + 5)$.

5. Use a table to evaluate each expression for different values of the variable.

a. Complete the table of values for each value of x.

x	$2x + 5$	$2(x + 5)$
0		
2		
4		
5		

b. What can you determine based on the values in the table?

6. Use the Distributive Property to rewrite the second expression.

7. Are the two expressions equivalent? Explain your reasoning.

8. Use the table of values to sketch the graph of both expressions on the coordinate plane.

a. Plot the values for each expression on the coordinate plane. Use a ☐ to represent the values from the first expression and a △ for the values from the second expression. Then, connect the results for each expression with a line.

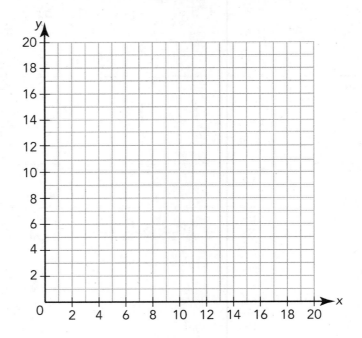

b. What does the graph tell you about the equivalence of the two expressions?

For each pair of expressions, use a table, properties, and a graph to determine if the expressions are equivalent.

9. $(3x + 8) + (6 - x)$ and $4x + 14$

a.

x	$(3x + 8) + (6 - x)$	$4x + 14$
0		
1		
2		

b. $(3x + 8) + (6 - x)$

$\qquad = (3x + 8) + (6 - x)$

$\qquad = 3x + (8 + 6) - x$

$\qquad = 3x + \underline{\hspace{1.5cm}} - x$

$\qquad = \underline{\hspace{1.5cm}} + 3x - x$

$\qquad = \underline{\hspace{1.5cm}}$

Given _____

Commutative Property of Addition _____

_____

Combine Like Terms _____

_____

_____

c.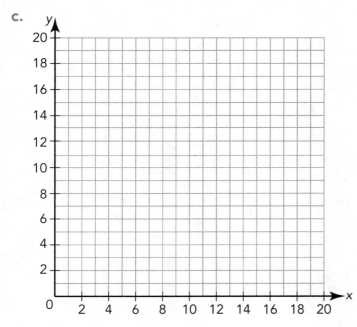

d. Are the two expressions equivalent? Explain using all three representations.

10. x + 3(2x + 1) and 7x + 3

a.

x	x + 3(2x + 1)	7x + 3
0		
1		
2		

b. x + 3 (2x + 1) _____ Given _____

   = x + _____ _____

   = _____ _____

c.

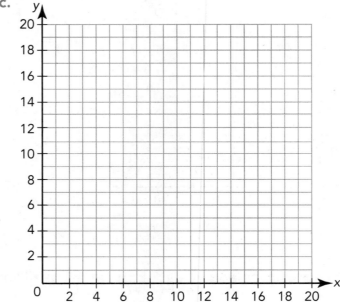

d. **Are the two expressions equivalent? Explain using all three representations.**

TALK the TALK

Property Management

For each step of the simplification of the expression, identify the property or operation applied.

Number Property or Operation

1. $10 \cdot 4x + 3(2x + 1)$ _____ Given _____

   $= (10 \cdot 4)x + 3(2x + 1)$ _____

   $= 40x + 3(2x + 1)$ _____ Multiplication _____

   $= 40x + 6x + 3$ _____

   $= 46x + 3$ _____

2. $20 + (6 + x) + 7$ _____ Given _____

   $= 20 + (x + 6) + 7$ _____

   $= 20 + x + (6 + 7)$ Associative Property of Addition

   $= 20 + x + 13$ _____

   $= x + 20 + 13$ _____

   $= x + 33$ _____

3. $7x + \frac{12x - 8}{4} + 5x$ _____ Given _____

   $= 7x + 3x - 2 + 5x$ _____

   $= 10x - 2 + 5x$ _____

   $= 10x + 5x - 2$ _____

   $= 15x - 2$ _____

4. Rewrite $\dfrac{2(x + 5) - 4}{2} - x$ using the fewest terms possible. Justify each step with a property or operation.

5. How can you use another representation to check that your answer in Question 4 is equivalent to $\dfrac{2(x + 5) - 4}{2} - x$?

Commutative Property of Addition	Associative Property of Multiplication	$a(b + c) = ab + ac$	
Distributive Property	Commutative Property of Multiplication	$(13 \cdot 2) \cdot 5 = 13 \cdot (2 \cdot 5)$	
$6 \cdot 5 = 5 \cdot 6$	Associative Property of Addition	$5(10 + 2) = 5 \cdot 10 + 5 \cdot 2$	
$a + b = b + a$	$x \cdot y = y \cdot x$	$(3 + 4) + 6 = 3 + (4 + 6)$	
$2 + 3 = 3 + 2$	$(j \cdot k) \cdot l = j \cdot (k \cdot l)$	$(l + m) + n = l + (m + n)$	

Assignment

Write

Match each term to the best definition.

1. Commutative Property of Addition
2. Commutative Property of Multiplication
3. Associative Property of Addition
4. Associative Property of Multiplication
5. like terms

a. For any numbers a and b, $a + b = b + a$

b. For any numbers a, b, and c,
   $(ab)c = a(bc)$

c. Two or more terms that have the same variable raised to the same power.

d. For any numbers a and b, $ab = ba$

e. For any numbers a, b, and c, $(a + b) + c = a + (b + c)$

6. Explain what it means for two expressions to be equivalent.

Remember

To determine whether two expressions are equivalent, you can create a table of values, graph the expressions, or rewrite the expressions using number properties.

Practice

Determine whether the two expressions are equivalent. Use properties, a table, and a graph in each problem to verify your answer.

1. $2(3x + 2) - 2x$ and $4x + 2$

2. $1 + 3(3 + x)$ and $4(3 + x)$

3. $2x + 1$ and $2\left(x + \frac{1}{2}\right)$

4. $\frac{(6x + 9)}{3} + 4$ and $2(x + 3.5)$

Stretch

Determine whether the two expressions are equivalent. Use properties, a table, and a graph in each problem to verify your answer.

1. $(x + 5)(2x + 1)$ and $2x^2 + 5$
2. $(x + 1)(x - 1)$ and $x^2 - 1$

Review

Use the Distributive Property and combine like terms to rewrite each expression.

1. $9(6m + 3) + 6(1 - 4m)$

2. $\dfrac{3(4x + 8y)}{6} + 2y - x$

Determine the better buy.

3. 6 car washes for $50 or 4 car washes for $36

4. 10 markers for $2.40 or 32 markers for $7.00

Determine the least common multiple (LCM) of each pair of numbers.

5. 6 and 10

6. 7 and 12

DVDs and Songs

Using Algebraic Expressions to Analyze and Solve Problems

WARM UP

Blake is twice as old as Alec.
Celia is 3 years older than Blake.

1. If Alec is 9 years old, how old is Blake?
2. If Alec is 9 years old, how old is Celia?
3. If Celia is 13 years old, how old is Blake?
4. If Celia is 13 years old, how old is Alec?
5. If Blake is 30 years old, how old is Alec?
6. If Blake is 30 years old, how old is Celia?

LEARNING GOALS

- Represent real-world problems with algebraic expressions.
- Use variables and write algebraic expressions to solve real-world and mathematical problems.

You have written numeric and algebraic expressions. How can algebraic expressions help you solve real-world problems?

Number Magic

Complete the number riddle by following each step.

Step 1: Pick a number between 1 and 30.
Step 2: Add 9 to your number.
Step 3: Multiply the sum by 3.
Step 4: Subtract 6 from the product.
Step 5: Divide the difference by 3.
Step 6: Subtract your original number.

You may need to complete the riddle a couple of times to get a sense of the pattern.

1. **Record your answer.**

2. **Compare your original number and your result with a classmate's number and result.**

3. **Use properties of numbers to demonstrate why the riddle works.**

Writing Expressions to Solve Problems

Jaret, Haley, Dillan, and Kierstin each collect DVDs. Jaret likes western movies, Haley likes comedies, Dillan likes action movies, and Kierstin likes science fiction movies.

Haley says: "I have twice as many DVDs as Jaret."

Dillan says: "I have four more DVDs than Haley."

Kierstin says: "I have three times as many as Dillan."

1. **If Jaret has 10 DVDs, determine the number of DVDs for each friend. Explain your reasoning.**

   Haley   **Dillan**

   Kierstin   **All four friends together**

2. **If Kierstin has 24 DVDs, determine the number of DVDs for each friend. Explain your reasoning.**

   Haley   **Dillan**

   Jaret   **All four friends together**

3. Let j represent the number of DVDs that Jaret has.

   a. Write an algebraic expression that represents the number of DVDs for each friend.

      Haley   Dillan

      Kierstin   All four friends together

> The number of DVDs that Dillan has is less than the number Kierstin has. So, the expression I write for Dillan has to be less than k.

   b. Use your expression from Question 3, part (a), to determine the number of DVDs they have altogether if Jaret has:

      10 DVDs.   2 DVDs.

      25 DVDs.   101 DVDs.

   c. Write an algebraic expression to represent the number of DVDs for:

      Jaret and Dillan   Haley and Kierstin

4. Let k represent the number of DVDs Kierstin has.

   a. Write an algebraic expression that represents the number of DVDs for each friend.

      Haley   Dillan

      Jaret   All four friends together

b. Use your expression from Question 6, part (a), to determine the number of DVDs they have altogether if Kierstin has:

72 DVDs.   24 DVDs.

36 DVDs.   660 DVDs.

c. Write an algebraic expression to represent the number of DVDs for:

Jaret and Dillan   Haley and Kierstin

5. Let h represent the number of DVDs Haley has.

a. Write an algebraic expression that represents the number of DVDs for each friend.

Jaret   Dillan

Kierstin   All four friends together

b. Use your expression from Question 9, part (a), to determine the number of DVDs they have altogether if Haley has:

20 DVDs.   24 DVDs.

50 DVDs.   34 DVDs.

c. Write an algebraic expression to represent the number of DVDs for:

Jaret and Dillan   Haley and Kierstin

6. Let d represent the number of DVDs Dillan has.

a. Write an algebraic expression that represents the number of DVDs for each friend.

Jaret   Haley

Kierstin   All four friends together

b. Use your expression from Question 11, part (a), to determine the number of DVDs they have altogether if Dillan has:

24 DVDs.   8 DVDs.

20 DVDs.   60 DVDs.

c. Write an algebraic expression to represent the number of DVDs for:

Jaret and Dillan   Haley and Kierstin

More Solving Problems with Expressions

Five friends have their own MP3 players.

Jake has 5 more songs on his MP3 than Rick has on his.

Marilyn has half as many songs on her MP3 as Jake has on his.

Lori has 3 more than twice the number of songs on her MP3 as Rick has on his.

Cody has 3 times as many songs on his MP3 as Marilyn has on hers.

1. Let *r* represent the number of songs on Rick's MP3 player. Write an algebraic expression that represents the number of songs on each friend's MP3 player.

   Jake   Marilyn

   Lori   Cody   All five friends together

2. Use your expression from Question 1 to calculate the number of songs they have altogether if Rick has:

   a. 15 songs.   b. 47 songs.

3. Write an algebraic expression to represent the number of songs for:

   a. Jake, Cody, and Rick   b. Marilyn and Lori

TALK the TALK 💬

Be a Magician!

You started this lesson by looking at a number riddle. Now that you have explored algebraic expressions, you can think about how they work.

1. Write the corresponding algebraic expressions for each step to show why this number trick works.

   - Choose a number.
   - Add 5.
   - Double the result.
   - Subtract 4.
   - Divide the result by 2.
   - Subtract the number you started with.
   - The result is 3.

2. Create your own number trick. Then write the corresponding algebraic expressions to show why it works.

Assignment

Write

How can algebraic expressions help you to solve real-world problems?

Remember

An algebraic expression is a mathematical phrase involving at least one variable and sometimes numbers and operation symbols.

Practice

At the end of each school year, Evan cleans out all of the school supplies that have collected in his desk. He can't believe how much stuff is in there this year! He has 4 times as many markers as he has pencils. He has 3 more highlighters than he has markers. He has twice as many pens as he has highlighters.

1. Suppose Evan found 5 pencils in his desk.
   a. Determine the number of markers that are in his desk. Explain your reasoning.
   b. Determine the number of highlighters that are in his desk. Explain your reasoning.
   c. Determine the number of pens that are in his desk. Explain your reasoning.
   d. Determine the total number of writing utensils that are in his desk. Explain your reasoning.

2. Suppose Evan found 78 pens in his desk.
   a. Determine the number of highlighters that are in his desk. Explain your reasoning.
   b. Determine the number of markers that are in his desk. Explain your reasoning.
   c. Determine the number of pencils that are in his desk. Explain your reasoning.
   d. Determine the total number of writing utensils that are in his desk. Explain your reasoning.

3. Let p represent the number of pencils that Evan has in his desk.
   a. Write an algebraic expression that represents the number of markers in Evan's desk.
   b. Write an algebraic expression that represents the number of highlighters in Evan's desk.
   c. Write an algebraic expression that represents the number of pens in Evan's desk.
   d. Write an algebraic expression that represents the total number of writing utensils in Evan's desk.
   e. Use your expression from part (d) to determine the total number of writing utensils in Evan's desk if there are 8 pencils.
   f. Use your expression to determine the total number of writing utensils in Evan's desk if there are 12 pencils.

Stretch

1. A three-digit number with all the same digits can be represented with an algebraic expression: $100 \times a + 10 \times a + a$. Use this fact to explain why any three-digit number with all repeated digits can be divided evenly by 37.

Review

Write an algebraic expression to represent each verbal expression.

1. One-third the sum of a number and two and one hundredths.

2. Sixteen and two-tenths subtracted from two times a number.

Calculate each percent.

3. In Ms. Romano's math class of 25 students, 8 of the students play a musical instrument. What percent of the class plays a musical instrument?

4. In Ms. Sobato's science class of 20 students, 3 of the students are in the school play. What percent of the class is in the school play?

Determine each whole for the percent and part given.

5. 68 is 32% of what number?

6. 16 is 80% of what number?

Expressions Summary

KEY TERMS

- power
- base
- exponent
- perfect square
- perfect cube
- evaluate a numeric expression
- Order of Operations
- variable
- algebraic expression
- coefficient
- term
- evaluate an algebraic expression
- like terms
- Distributive Property
- equivalent expressions

LESSON 1 — Relationships Matter

Repeated multiplication can be represented as a power. A **power** has two elements: the base and the exponent. The **base** of a power is the factor that is multiplied repeatedly in the power, and the **exponent** of the power is the number of times the base is used as a factor.

$$2 \times 2 \times 2 \times 2 = 2^4$$

You can read this power in different ways: "2 to the fourth power," "2 raised to the fourth power," or "2 to the fourth."

A number multiplied by itself is a square. The squares of integers are called **perfect squares**. For example, 9 is a perfect square because $3 \times 3 = 9$. Another way to write this equation is $3^2 = 9$. You can read 3^2 as "3 squared."

A number used as a factor three times is a cube. A **perfect cube** is the cube of an integer. For example, 216 is a perfect cube because $6 \times 6 \times 6$, or 6^3, is equal to 216. You can read 6^3 as "6 cubed."

To **evaluate a numeric expression** means to simplify the expression to a single numeric value.

For example, consider the numeric expression $2 \cdot 5^2$ represented by the model shown.

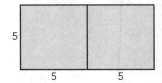

$5^2 = 25$, and $2 \cdot 5^2 = 2 \cdot 25$, or 50.

Therefore, $2 \cdot 5^2$ has a value of 50.

The **Order of Operations** is a set of rules that ensures the same result every time an expression is evaluated.
1. Evaluate expressions inside parentheses or grouping symbols.
2. Evaluate exponents.
3. Multiply and divide from left to right.
4. Add and subtract from left to right.

For example, evaluate the expression $12 \div (4 + 2) + 4^2$ using the Order of Operations.

$12 \div (6) + 4^2$	Evaluate the expression in parentheses.
$12 \div 6 + 16$	Evaluate the exponent.
$2 + 16$	Divide from left to right.
18	Add from left to right.

**LESSON
2**

Into the Unknown

In mathematics, letters are often used to represent quantities that vary. These letters are called **variables**, and they help you write algebraic expressions to represent situations. An **algebraic expression** is an expression that has at least one variable.

For example, if a school lunch costs $2.25 for each student, you can write an algebraic expression to represent the total amount of money collected for any number of students buying school lunches.

The variable s can represent the unknown number of students buying school lunches. The algebraic expression is $2.25s$.

A number that is multiplied by a variable in an algebraic expression is called the numerical **coefficient**. The coefficient in the expression written above is 2.25.

A **term** of an algebraic expression is a number, variable, or product of numbers and variables.

For example, consider the expression $3x + 4y - 7$. The expression has three terms: $3x$, $4y$, and 7. The operation between the first two terms is addition, and the operation between the second and third term is subtraction. There are two terms with variables and the third term is a constant term of 7.

To **evaluate an algebraic expression** means to determine the value of the expression for a given value of each variable. When you evaluate an algebraic expression, you substitute the given values for the variables, and then determine the value of the expression.

For example, evaluate $10 - \frac{x}{3}$, for $x = 9$.

$10 - \frac{9}{3}$ Substitute the given value for x.

$10 - 3 = 7$ Use the Order of Operations to evaluate the expression.

In an algebraic expression, **like terms** are two or more terms that have the same variable raised to the same power. The numerical coefficients of like terms may be different. You can combine like terms in algebraic expressions by adding or subtracting terms with the same variables. For example, $3x + 5x$ combines to make $8x$.

Algebraic expressions can be rewritten using the **Distributive Property**.

For example, consider the expression $5(x + 1)$, which has two factors: 5 and the quantity $(x + 1)$. In this case, multiply the 5 by each term of the quantity $(x + 1)$. The model using algebra tiles is shown.

$5(x + 1) = 5x + 5$

You can also rewrite an expression of the form $\frac{4x + 8}{4}$ using the Distributive Property.

$$\frac{4x + 8}{4} = \frac{4x}{4} + \frac{8}{4}$$
$$= 1x + 2$$
$$= x + 2$$

The Distributive Property can also be used to rewrite an algebraic expression as a product of two factors: a constant and a sum of terms. This is also referred to as factoring expressions.

To rewrite the expression $4x - 7$ so the coefficient of the variable is 1, factor out the coefficient 4 from each term. The equivalent expression is the product of the coefficient and the sum of the remaining factors.

$$4x - 7 = 4\left(\frac{4x}{4} - \frac{7}{4}\right)$$
$$= 4\left(x - \frac{7}{4}\right)$$

LESSON
4

Are They Saying the Same Thing?

Two algebraic expressions are **equivalent expressions** if, when any values are substituted for the variables, the results are equal.

Creating a table of values, graphing the expressions, or rewriting the expressions using number properties can help you to determine if two expressions are equivalent.

For example, consider the two expressions $3(x + 1) - 2x$ and $x + 3$.

The table of values for each value of x shows that the two expressions are equivalent.

Using the table of values to graph the two expressions results in two lines that lie on top of one another, showing that the expressions are equivalent.

x	$3(x + 1) - 2x$	$x + 3$
0	3	3
1	4	4
2	5	5
3	6	6

You can also rewrite the given expression to show that the two expressions are equivalent.

$3(x + 1) - 2x$	Given
$3x + 3 - 2x$	Distributive Property
$x + 3$	Combine Like Terms

LESSON 5

DVDs and Songs

You can use algebraic expressions to represent, analyze, and solve real-world problems. For example, let k represent the number of books that Karen has.

Jack has three times as many books as Karen: $3k$.

Daniel has 6 more books than Jack: $3k + 6$.

Hannah has twice as many books as Daniel: $2(3k + 6)$.

If Karen has 10 books, determine the total number of books the four friends have together.

Substitute 10 for k in each expression to determine the number of books each friend has.

Jack has $3 \cdot 10$, or 30 books.
Daniel has $3 \cdot 10 + 6$, or 36 books.
Hannah has $2(3 \cdot 10 + 6)$, or 72 books.

The total number of books the four friends have together is $10 + 30 + 36 + 72 = 148$ books.

TOPIC 2
Equations

In a tug-of-war contest, one side may be stronger, so the two sides would be unequal. Or both sides could be equally strong. No matter what, these two puppies = cute.

Module 3: Determining Unknown Quantities

TOPIC 2: EQUATIONS

In this topic, students use their understanding of expressions to create equations and determine if given values are solutions to equations or simple inequalities. Students develop an understanding of the equals sign as indicating a relationship, not as an operator. They learn that solving an equation means maintaining equality of the expressions on either side of the equals sign. Students analyze equations and generalize that equations can have one solution, no solution, or infinitely many solutions. Students use bar models to reason about solving one-step addition and multiplication equations. Bar models are used to emphasize the importance of maintaining equality. Students solve a variety of real-world problems by writing and solving one-step addition and multiplication equations.

Where have we been?

In the previous topic, students learned about expressions. Instruction in this topic asks students to set expressions equal to each other and to determine if they are equal. Students have been solving for missing values in addition and subtraction equations since grade 1 and in multiplication and division equations since grade 3. However, this topic is likely the first time they have used variables to represent and solve for an unknown value in an equation.

Where are we going?

In grade 7, students will expand their ability to solve equations to two-step linear equations. By grade 8, students will be able to solve a wide variety of linear equations. In high school, students will expand their skills to include solving exponential, quadratic, polynomial, and trigonometric equations. All of this work is built upon the foundation of equivalent expressions that students begin to build in this topic.

Using Bar Models to Solve Addition Equations

Bar models are visual tools that can be used to solve equations. For example, this bar model shows that the expressions $x + 10$ and 15 are equal, so $x + 10 = 15$. The top bar can be split into two bars, x and 10. When this split happens in the bottom bar, with one bar containing 10, it shows that x is the same as 5, so $x = 5$.

x	10
$x + 10$	
15	
5	10

Myth: "Just give me the rule. If I know the rule, then I understand the math."

Memorize the following rule: *All quars are elos.* Will you remember that rule tomorrow? Nope. Why not? Because it has no meaning. It isn't connected to anything you know. What if we change the rule to: *All squares are parallelograms*. How about now? Can you remember that? Of course you can because now it makes sense.

Learning does not take place in a vacuum. It **must be** connected to what you already know. Otherwise, arbitrary rules will be forgotten.

#mathmythbusted

Talking Points

You can further support your student's learning by making sure they eat right and get enough sleep. Healthy bodies make for healthy minds, and both diet and sleep have significant effects on learning.

Key Terms

equation
An equation is a mathematical sentence that contains an equals sign. An equation can contain numbers, variables, or both in the same mathematical sentence.

inverse operations
Inverse operations are pairs of operations that undo the effects of each other.

First Among Equals

1

Reasoning with Equal Expressions

WARM UP

Rewrite each number as an addition, subtraction, multiplication, or division expression. Use each operation once.

1. 24

2. $\frac{1}{2}$

3. 0

4. 100

LEARNING GOALS

- Compose and decompose numeric and algebraic equations.
- Substitute values into equations to determine whether they make the equation true.
- Construct and analyze equations using Properties of Equality.
- Analyze, write, and graph inequalities.
- Determine the number of solutions of an equation or inequality.

KEY TERMS

- equation
- Reflexive Property of Equality
- solution
- Addition Property of Equality
- Subtraction Property of Equality
- Multiplication Property of Equality
- Division Property of Equality
- Symmetric Property of Equality
- Zero Property of Multiplication
- Identity Property of Multiplication
- Identity Property of Addition
- graph of an inequality
- solution set of an inequality

You have learned about both numeric and algebraic expressions and how they describe situations and relationships among quantities. What properties do equal expressions have and how can you use these properties to reason about solutions?

The Same But Different

1. Write different expressions equal to 4.

   _____ = 4

   4 = _____

   4 = _____

Be creative! Include different operations in your expressions.

2. Now write different expressions equal to 4 + 5.

   4 + 5 = _____

   _____ = 4 + 5

   4 + 5 = _____

3. What can you do to one of the expressions you wrote in Question 1 to make it equal to one of the expressions you wrote in Question 2?

Using Substitution to Understand Equality

An **equation** is a statement of equality between two expressions. An equation can contain numbers, variables, or both in the same mathematical sentence.

Consider the equation $8 + 4 = \_\_ + 5$. It has an unknown number.

One way to determine the unknown number is to rewrite the expressions on both sides of the equals sign until they match.

Consider each reasoning strategy that is used to determine the unknown number in $8 + 4 = \_\_ + 5$.

> The Reflexive Property of Equality says that when both sides of an equation look exactly the same, their values are equal.

Rylee

The equal sign tells me to perform the operation on the left in the equation $8 + 4 = \_\_ + 5$.

$$8 + 4 = 12 + 5$$

$$12 + 5 = 17$$

Therefore, the unknown number is 17.

Clover

I can determine the unknown number in $8 + 4 = \_\_ + 5$ by rewriting the expression on the left. I can take 1 from 8 and give it to the 4 and keep the value of the expression the same.

$$(8 - 1) + (4 + 1) = \_\_ + 5$$

$$7 + 5 = \_\_ + 5$$

Therefore, the unknown number is 7.

Fiona

I can determine the unknown number in 8 + 4 = ___ + 5 by rewriting both expressions.

$$8 + 4 = \text{\_\_\_} + 1 + 4$$

$$7 + 1 + 4 = \text{\_\_\_} + 1 + 4$$

Therefore, the unknown number is 7.

1. What is the unknown number in the equation 8 + 4 = ___ + 5? Explain how this makes sense.

2. Explain the error in Rylee's reasoning.

3. How are Clover's reasoning and Fiona's reasoning similar? How are they different?

4. Consider the equation $31 + 67 = \underline{\hspace{1cm}} + 12$.

   a. Determine the unknown number by rewriting the expressions on either side of the equals sign until they match.

   b. How can you check your answer to make sure it is correct?

   c. What number property or properties did you use when determining the unknown number?

5. Use your number sense reasoning to determine each unknown number. Show your work.

   a. $85 + 45 = \underline{\hspace{1cm}} + 60$ b. $9 + 23 = \underline{\hspace{1cm}} + 14$

ACTIVITY 1.2 · Solutions from a Set

Equations come in many forms. Because expressions are either numeric or algebraic, equations can be made of just numbers or both numbers and variables.

Equations are statements—they may be always true, never true, or true only for one or more values of the variable.

Always True	Never True	True for certain values of the variable
$6 = 10 - 4$	$10 = 20$	$x = 5$
$x = x$	$x = x + 2$	$x + 2 = 12$

When you determine that an equation is never true, you can make it a true statement by using the symbol ≠. For example, $10 = 20$ should be written as $10 \neq 20$.

Expressions
$6 - 2$
x
4
$2(x + 1)$
$0 + 8$
$2x$
$2x + 2$
8
$3x$
0

1. **Create at least five different kinds of equations using the list of expressions given.**

2. **Identify your equations that are always true, never true, and those equations where you don't yet know whether they are true or false. Explain your reasoning.**

A **solution** to an equation is any value for a variable that makes the equation true.

3. Sets of values are given. For each set, decide which value(s), if any, makes each of your equations from Question 1 true. Show your work.

   a. {1, 2, 3, 4}

   b. {1, 3, 5, 7, 9}

   c. {0}

4. Use the list of given expressions to write the type of equation described.

   a. Write an equation with variables that has no possible solution. Explain why the equation has no solution.

   b. Write an equation with variables that is true no matter what number is substituted for the variable. Explain why there are an infinite number of solutions.

ACTIVITY 1.3 Using Properties of Equality

The **Addition Property of Equality** states that if two values a and b are equal, when you add the same value c to each, the sums are equal.

The **Subtraction Property of Equality** states that when you subtract the same value c from equal values a and b, the differences are equal.

Properties of Equality	For all numbers a, b, and c
Addition Property of Equality	If $a = b$, then $a + c = b + c$.
Subtraction Property of Equality	If $a = b$, then $a - c = b - c$.

1. Suppose you have the equation $x = 15$.

    a. Use the Addition Property of Equality to write at least 3 equations that have the same solution.

    b. Use the Subtraction Property of Equality to write at least 3 equations that have the same solution.

2. Suppose you have the equation $x + 5 = 1 + 9$.

    a. Use the Addition Property of Equality to write at least 3 equations that have the same solution.

    b. Use the Subtraction Property of Equality to write at least 3 equations that have the same solution.

The **Multiplication Property of Equality** states that if two values a and b are equal, when you multiply each by the same value c, the products are equal. The **Division Property of Equality** states that when you divide equal values a and b by the same value c, the quotients are equal. The Division Property of Equality is true only if c is not equal to 0.

Properties of Equality	For all numbers a, b, and c
Multiplication Property of Equality	If $a = b$, then $a \cdot c = b \cdot c$.
Division Property of Equality	If $a = b$ and $c \neq 0$, then $a \div c = b \div c$.

Why can't the value of c be 0?

3. **Suppose you have the equation $x = 5$.**

   a. **Use the Multiplication Property of Equality to write at least 3 equations that have the same solution.**

   b. **Use the Division Property of Equality to write at least 3 equations that have the same solution.**

4. **Suppose you have the equation $\frac{1}{2}x = 10$.**

   a. **Use the Multiplication Property of Equality to write at least 3 equations that have the same solution.**

   b. **Use the Division Property of Equality to write at least 3 equations that have the same solution.**

Properties of Equality are logical rules that allow you to maintain balance and rewrite equations.

5. **Describe how you can check the solutions of the equations you wrote in Questions 1 and 3.**

The **Symmetric Property of Equality** states that if $a = b$, then $b = a$. So, $x = 3$ is the same as $3 = x$.

Cut out the cards at the end of the lesson. There are Equation Cards and Solution Cards. The Solution Cards are shaded blue.

1. **Match the Equation Cards with the Solution Cards. Explain how you identified each solution.**

2. **Which equation(s) have no solutions? Explain how you know.**

3. **Which equation(s) have an infinite number of solutions? Explain how you know.**

Equations that have an infinite number of solutions are equations that are true no matter what value you assign to the variable. These kinds of equations often describe important properties of numbers.

Consider each property.

- The **Zero Property of Multiplication** states that the product of any number and 0 is 0.

- The **Identity Property of Multiplication** states that the product of any number and 1 is the number.

- The **Identity Property of Addition** states that the sum of any number and 0 is the number.

4. Study the Equation Cards.

   a. Which equation(s) states the Zero Property of Multiplication?

   b. Which equation(s) states the Identity Property of Multiplication?

   c. Which equation(s) states the Identity Property of Addition?

5. Three of the Solution Cards did not match any of the Equation Cards. Write equations that have those values as solutions.

ACTIVITY 1.5 Inequalities

You can use a number line to represent inequalities. The **graph of an inequality** in one variable is the set of all points on a number line that make the inequality true. The set of all points that make an inequality true is the **solution set of the inequality**.

1. Consider the graphs of the inequalities $x > 3$ and $x \geq 3$.

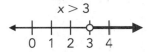

$x > 3$

$x \geq 3$

a. Describe each number line representation.

Why does one graph show an open point and the other one a closed point?

b. Describe the solution set for each inequality.

c. How does the solution set of the inequality $x \geq 3$ differ from the solution set of $x > 3$?

2. Consider the graphs of the inequalities $x < 3$ and $x \leq 3$.

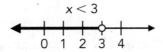

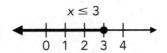

   a. Describe each number line representation.

   b. Describe the solution set for each.

   c. How does the solution set of the inequality $x \leq 3$ differ
      from the solution set of $x < 3$?

The solution to any inequality can be represented on a number line
by a ray. A ray begins at a starting point and goes on forever in
one direction.

A closed circle means that the starting point is part of the solution
set of the inequality. An open circle means that the starting point is
not part of the solution set of the inequality.

3. Write the inequality represented by each graph.

a.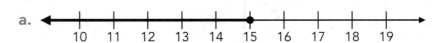

b.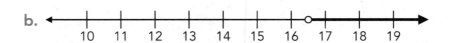

c.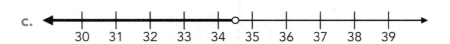

d.

4. Graph the solution set for each inequality.

a. $x \leq 14$

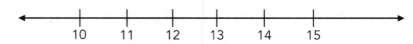

b. $x < 55$

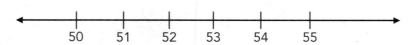

c. $2\frac{1}{2} \leq x$

d. $x > 3.3$

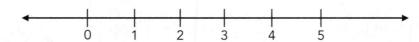

e. $x \neq 4.2$

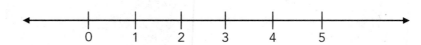

5. Consider the inequalities in Questions 1 through 4.

    a. How many solutions does each inequality have?

    b. Can you write an inequality that has no solutions? Explain.

    c. Can you write an inequality that has just one solution?
       Explain your reasoning.

6. Explain the meaning of each sentence in words. Then, define a variable and write a mathematical statement to represent each statement. Finally, sketch a graph of each inequality.

    a. The maximum load for an elevator is 2900 lbs.

    b. A car can seat up to 8 passengers.

    c. No persons under the age of 18 are permitted.

    d. You must be at least 13 years old to join.

> Does a "maximum" include the starting point?

TALK the TALK

Not All Variables Are Created Equal

A point at *a* is plotted on the number line shown.

1. Plot a point to the right of this point and label it *b*.

   a. Write three different inequalities that are true about *a* and *b*.

   b. What can you say about all points to the right of point *a* on the number line?

2. Plot a point to the left of *a* and label it *c*.

   a. Write three different inequalities that are true about *a* and *c*.

   b. What can you say about all the points to the left of point *a* on the number line?

3. Describe the position of all the points on the number line that are:

   a. greater than *a*.   b. less than *a*.

Equation Cards

$11 + x = 11$	$10x = 30$	$\dfrac{x}{3} + 10 = 20$	$x + 3.5 = 14.25$	$\dfrac{1}{8}x = 8$
$1x + 6 = 9$	$x + 1 = x$	$\dfrac{5}{8} = x + \dfrac{1}{2}$	$x - 5 = x - 4$	$\dfrac{x}{9} = 2$
$5 = x + 5$	$29 = x \cdot 29$	$\dfrac{x}{10} = 0.1$	$45 = 5x$	$\dfrac{10}{x} = 0.1$
$x \cdot 1 = x$	$x + 0 = x$	$x + 4 = 4 + x$	$\dfrac{x}{4} = \dfrac{1}{4}x$	$0x = 0$

Solution Cards

$x = 10.75$	$x = 0$	$3 = x$	no solutions	$x = \dfrac{1}{8}$
$x = 18$	$30 = x$	$x = 100$	$6 = x$ (six)	$x = 1$
$9 = x$ (nine)	$x = \dfrac{1}{4}$	$64 = x$	infinite solutions	$x = 0.1$

Assignment

Write

Complete each statement with the correct term.

1. The _____ states that if two values *a* and *b* are equal, when you multiply each by the same value *c*, the products are equal.
2. A _____ to an equation is any value for a variable that makes the equation true.
3. The _____ says that when both sides of an equation look exactly the same, their values must be equal.
4. An _____ is a mathematical sentence created by writing two expressions with an equals sign between them.
5. The _____ is the set of all points on a number line that make the inequality true.

Remember

Properties of Equality are logical rules that allow you to maintain balance and rewrite equations.

Properties of Equality	For all numbers *a*, *b*, and *c*
Addition Property of Equality	If $a = b$, then $a + c = b + c$.
Subtraction Property of Equality	If $a = b$, then $a - c = b - c$.
Multiplication Property of Equality	If $a = b$, then $ac = bc$.
Division Property of Equality	If $a = b$, and $c \neq 0$, then $\frac{a}{c} = \frac{b}{c}$.

Practice

Indicate whether each equation has one solution, no solutions, or an infinite number of solutions and explain your reasoning. If the equation has one solution, determine the solution from the set of values given.

Set of values: {0, 1, 2, 3, 4, 5, 9, 10, 35, 36, 37, 38, 39, 40, 50, 60, 61, 62, 63, 64, 65, 99, 100}

1. $x - 3 = x + 3$
2. $4 \cdot x = 20$
3. $81 = 9x$
4. $x + 17 = 55$
5. $\frac{x}{3} = 21$
6. $1x = x$
7. $8 + x = x + 8$
8. $99 = x - 1$

Stretch

Model each equality or inequality situation. Then determine each solution.

1. Najid is taller than Emily and shorter than Daniel. Who is the tallest?
2. Sophie is now as old as Jasmine was 6 years ago. Who is older?

Review

1. Define variables and write an algebraic expression to represent each situation.
   a. Miguel has three times as many books as Jose.
   b. Rosa has 5 fewer bracelets than Maria.

For each situation, examine the given expressions and/or solution strategies.

2. Darian's band made $500 on one night. They had to subtract costs of $80 and then divide the remaining money among the band members. If there are 4 members in the band, which numeric expression correctly shows the amount that each member will make? Explain your answer using the rules for order of operations.

Expression A

$500 - 80 \div 4$

Expression B

$(500 - 80) \div 4$

3. Darian's band hires a manager. The manager asks a local park if they can hold a concert on one of the lawn areas. The lawn can have 20 rows of seats with 20 chairs in each row. The band charges $25 for each seat. The cost for advertising, the rental of the chairs, and the management fees totals $4000. If the band is able to fill all of the seats, which solution shows the amount the band will make? Determine the error that was made in the incorrect solution.

Solution A

$25 \times 20^2 - 4000$

$25 \times 400 - 4000$

$10,000 - 4000$

6000

Solution B

$25 \times 20^2 - 4000$

$500^2 - 4000$

$250,000 - 4000$

$246,000$

4. Determine each unknown.

a. $\dfrac{5}{6} = \dfrac{x}{30}$

b. $\dfrac{90}{x} = \dfrac{9}{2}$

Bar None

2

Solving One-Step Addition Equations

WARM UP

Determine each sum or difference.

1. $5.67 + 8.73$

2. $8.73 - 5.67$

3. $\frac{3}{7} + \frac{4}{5}$

4. $\frac{20}{3} - \frac{15}{4}$

LEARNING GOALS

- Reason about addition equations.
- Use bar models to represent one-step addition equations.
- Use inverse operations to solve one-step addition equations.
- Solve one-step addition equations.

KEY TERMS

- bar model
- one-step equation
- inverse operations

Throughout this course, you have used a variety of tools to solve mathematical problems, including area models, pictures, tables, tape diagrams, double number lines, graphs, and expressions. What tools might help you in solving equations?

Form of 0

Consider the number 0. What comes to mind?

1. Write five different numeric expressions for the number 0.

Be creative! Use different types of numbers and operations in your expressions.

Share your numeric expressions with your classmates.

2. Did you and your classmates use common strategies to write your expressions? How many possible numeric expressions could you write for this number?

ACTIVITY 2.1

Reasoning About Addition Equations

Reasoning about equations and determining solutions with *bar models* provides a visual representation of the structure of the equations. A **bar model** uses rectangular bars to represent known and unknown quantities.

WORKED EXAMPLE

Consider the addition equation $x + 10 = 15$.

$x + 10$
15

This equation states that for some value of x, the expression $x + 10$ is equal to 15. This can be represented using a bar model.

Just like with area models, bar models can be decomposed. The expression $x + 10$ can be decomposed into a part representing x and a part representing 10. The number 15 can be decomposed in a similar way: $15 = 5 + 10$.

x	10

$x + 10$

15

5	10

The bar model demonstrates that these two equations are equivalent.

$$x + 10 = 15$$
$$x + 10 = 5 + 10$$

By examining the structure of the second equation, you can see that 5 is the value for x that makes this equation true.

1. Why is the number 15 decomposed into the numeric expression 5 + 10?

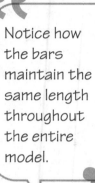

Notice how the bars maintain the same length throughout the entire model.

2. Describe how the model in the worked example would be different for each equation. Complete the bar model for each.

a. x + 10 = 17

x	10

x + 10

17

b. x + 6 = 15

x	

x + 6

15

3. Consider the equation 14 + x = 32.

a. Complete the bar model.

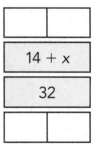

14 + x

32

b. Write the equation represented by the decomposed expressions in the bar model.

c. Which value for x makes the equation a true statement?

4. Consider the equation $90 = x + 64$.

   a. Complete the bar model.

   b. Write the expression represented by the decomposed expressions in the bar model.

   c. Which value for x makes the equation a true statement?

5. In each bar model, how did you determine how to decompose the given expressions?

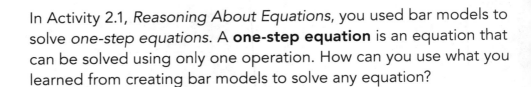

ACTIVITY 2.2 Solving Addition Equations

In Activity 2.1, *Reasoning About Equations*, you used bar models to solve *one-step equations*. A **one-step equation** is an equation that can be solved using only one operation. How can you use what you learned from creating bar models to solve any equation?

Now that you understand the bar model, you can write equivalent equations with the same structure. While you can use reasoning to determine the value for the variable that makes an equation true, you can also use the properties and *inverse operations* to isolate the variable. **Inverse operations** are pairs of operations that reverse the effects of each other. For example, subtraction and addition are inverse operations.

> The Additive Identity Property states that for any number m, $m + 0 = m$. In other words, when you add 0 to any number, it stays the same. It keeps its identity!

WORKED EXAMPLE

Solve the equation $h + 6 = 19$.

$$h + 6 = 13 + 6$$ Write equivalent expressions that mirror structure.

$$h + 6 - 6 = 13 + 6 - 6$$ Use inverse operations to reverse the addition of 6 to h.

$$h + 0 = 13 + 0$$ Combine like terms and apply the Additive Identity Property.

$$h = 13$$

1. Examine the worked example.

    a. What is the solution to $h + 6 = 19$?

    b. Are there other solutions to the equation? How do you know?

2. Use the same strategy to solve each equation.

    a. $35 = 12 + m$ b. $t + 24 = 85$

3. Analyze Kaniah's strategy to solve the equation $11 = m + 7$.

Kaniah
When solving the addition equation $11 = m + 7$, I can simply subtract 7 from both sides without first writing an equivalent equation.

$$11 = m + 7$$
$$11 - 7 = m + 7 - 7$$
$$4 = m$$

The value for m that makes this equation true is 4.

    a. What Property of Equality is Kaniah using in her strategy?

    b. How could Kaniah check that her solution is correct?

4. Use Kaniah's strategy to solve each equation. Check to see that your solution makes the original equation a true statement.

a. $120 + y = 315$

b. $5\frac{3}{4} = x + 4\frac{1}{2}$

c. $b + 5.67 = 12.89$

d. $2356 = a + 1699$

e. $\frac{7}{12} = g + \frac{1}{4}$

f. $w + 3.14 = 27$

g. $13\frac{7}{8} = c + 9\frac{3}{4}$

h. $19 + p = 105$

Reasoning About More Interesting Addition Equations

1. Braeden thinks that he can use decomposition to reason about more complicated equations, such as $4x = 20 + 3x$.

   Is Braeden correct? Show your work.

2. Think about each algebraic equation. Use reasoning to describe a relationship between c and d that makes the mathematical sentence true.

   a. $c + 23 = d + 14$ b. $45 + c = 66 + d$

   c. $c + 3d = 2c$ d. $4c + d + 10 = 8c + 2d$

TALK the TALK

It All Adds Up

1. What does it mean to solve an equation?

2. Describe how to solve any one-step addition equation. How do you check to see if a value is the solution to an equation?

3. Write two different one-step equations for each solution provided.

   a. $m = 12$

   b. $5 = x$

   c. $5.6 = h$

   d. $j = 6\frac{4}{7}$

Assignment

Write

Write a definition for each term in your own words.

- one-step equation
- solution
- inverse operations

Remember

A solution to an equation is the value or values for the variable that makes the equation true. To solve a one-step addition equation, isolate the variable using number sense or the Subtraction Property of Equality.

Practice

Use a bar model to solve each equation.

1. $x + 7 = 15$

2. $19 = x + 13$

3. $14.5 = 6 + y$

4. $a + \frac{1}{2} = 4\frac{3}{4}$

Solve each equation. Check each solution.

5. $34 = x + 17$

6. $a + 25 = 92$

7. $7\frac{3}{5} + b = 10\frac{3}{4}$

8. $24\frac{1}{2} = t + 5\frac{1}{4}$

9. $r + 3.4 = 13.1$

10. $4.21 = 2.98 + s$

Stretch

Solve each equation. Check each solution.

1. $34 = x - 17$

2. $a - 25 = 92$

3. $r - 3.4 = 13.1$

4. $24\frac{1}{2} = t - 5\frac{1}{4}$

Review

Use the Properties of Equality to write 2 equations that have the given solution. Identify which property of equality was used.

1. $j = 3$

2. $8 = m$

Define variables and write an algebraic expression to represent each situation.

3. Terrance has one fewer sibling than Casey. Kolbie has three more siblings than Terrance.
4. Connor has half as many comic books as Devyn. Isaac has 4 more comic books than Connor.

Rewrite each expression.

5. $\frac{2}{3}x + \frac{4}{5}x$

6. $\frac{1}{3}\left(\frac{2}{5}x\right)$

Play It In Reverse

Solving One-Step Multiplication Equations

3

LEARNING GOALS

- Use bar models to represent one-step multiplication equations.
- Use inverse operations to solve one-step multiplication equations.
- Reason about multiplication equations.
- Connect bar models to the algorithm for solving multiplication equations.
- Solve one-step multiplication equations.

You have solved one-step addition equations using bar models and inverse operations. How can you use similar strategies to solve one-step multiplication problems?

Form of 1

Consider the number 1. What comes to mind?

1. Write five different numeric expressions for the number 1.

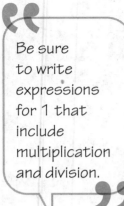

Be sure to write expressions for 1 that include multiplication and division.

Share your numeric expressions with your classmates.

2. Did you and your classmates use common strategies to write your expressions? How many possible numeric expressions could you write for this number?

Reasoning About Multiplication Equations

Just as with addition equations, solving multiplication equations involves determining the value for the variable that makes the statement true. You can use bar models to understand the structure of the equation and reason about the solution.

WORKED EXAMPLE

Consider the multiplication equation $2x = 6$.

This equation states that for some value of x, the expression $2x$ is equal to 6.

You can decompose $2x$ by rewriting it as the equivalent expression $1x + 1x$, or $x + x$.

To maintain equivalence, decompose 6 in a similar way.

The bar model demonstrates that these two equations are equivalent.

$$2x = 6$$

$$x + x = 3 + 3$$

By examining the structure of the second equation, you can see that $x = 3$.

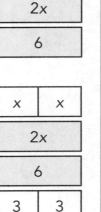

How do these bar models relate to the bar models you used to solve addition equations?

1. Why is the number 6 decomposed into the numeric expression $3 + 3$?

Solve each equation using a bar model.

2. $3x = 12$

3. $7x = 63$

4. $4x = 6$

Solving Equations with Fractional Coefficients

Multiplication equations often include numbers other than whole numbers.

Consider the equation $\frac{1}{3}x = 2$.

Remember there are different ways to write equivalent expressions.

$$\frac{1}{3}x = \frac{x}{3}$$

1. **Explain how this equation compares to the equations in the previous activity.**

WORKED EXAMPLE

Represent $\frac{1}{3}x = 2$ as a bar model.

$\frac{1}{3}x$
2

To solve this equation for x, compose 3 equally-sized parts to create the whole, x.

To maintain equivalence, compose 3 equally-sized parts for the other expression, too.

This structure allows you to see the value of x.

x		
$\frac{1}{3}x$	$\frac{1}{3}x$	$\frac{1}{3}x$
2		

Because you start with a fractional amount of x, you have to compose to get a whole x.

---

2. **Complete the worked example by filling in the missing values. Then write the solution to the equation $\frac{1}{3}x = 2$.**

Solve each equation using a bar model.

3. $\frac{1}{4}x = 7$

4. $\frac{x}{2} = 5$

5. Consider how to use bar models to solve $\frac{2}{3}x = 8$.
   Analyze each strategy.

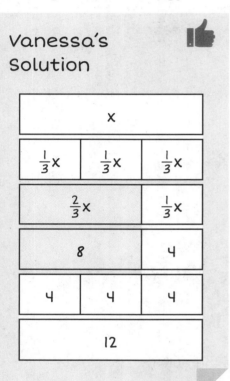

Vanessa's Solution

| x |
$\frac{1}{3}x$	$\frac{1}{3}x$	$\frac{1}{3}x$
$\frac{2}{3}x$	$\frac{1}{3}x$
8	4
4	4	4
12

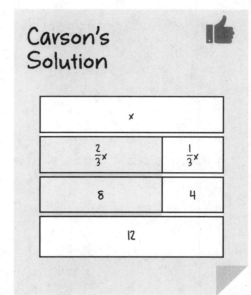

Carson's Solution

| x |
| $\frac{2}{3}x$ | $\frac{1}{3}x$ |
| 8 | 4 |
| 12 |

This reminds me of tape diagrams.

a. How is Carson's solution strategy different from Vanessa's solution strategy?

b. What reasoning might Vanessa have used in her solution strategy?

Solve each equation using a bar model.

6. $\frac{4}{5}x = 12$

7. $\frac{3}{4}x = 8$

8. Consider the equation $\frac{8}{5}x = 64$.

   a. How does this fractional coefficient compare to the fractional coefficients that you have seen in this lesson so far?

   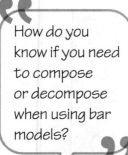

   How do you know if you need to compose or decompose when using bar models?

   b. Create a bar model and solve for x.

Reflect on the equations you solved in this activity.

9. How were they similar? What was common in how you used the bar models?

Solving More Complex Multiplication Equations

Consider the equation $\frac{4}{5}x = \frac{1}{10}$.

1. How is this equation different from the equation you solved in the previous activity?

Compare the two solution strategies proposed by Landon and Zoe.

Landon's Solution

$\frac{4}{5}x = \frac{1}{10}$

Scale $\frac{4}{5}$ up to $\frac{8}{10}$.

$\frac{8}{10}x = \frac{1}{10}$

$8x = 1$

1x	1x	1x	1x	1x	1x	1x	1x

8x

1

$\frac{1}{8}$	$\frac{1}{8}$	$\frac{1}{8}$	$\frac{1}{8}$	$\frac{1}{8}$	$\frac{1}{8}$	$\frac{1}{8}$	$\frac{1}{8}$

Zoe's Solution

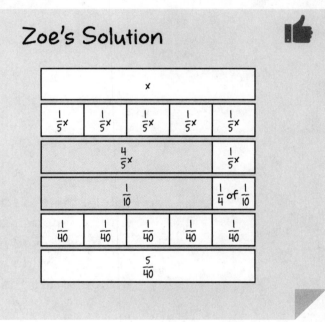

2. Explain Landon's solution strategy.

    a. What type of reasoning did Landon use at the beginning of his solution?

    b. How did he know to write $8x = 1$?

    c. Will scaling up always work?

3. Explain how Zoe's solution is similar to the other equations you have solved with bar models.

Use a bar model to solve each equation.

4. $\frac{3}{4}x = \frac{2}{5}$

5. $\frac{2}{7}x = \frac{4}{9}$

6. You learned to solve addition equations by first reasoning with bar models and then with inverse operations. Now that you have solved multiplication equations by reasoning with bar models, how do you think that you can solve these equations without using the bar models?

ACTIVITY 3.4 · Solving Multiplication Equations Without Models

Like addition equations, all of the multiplication equations you have modeled in this lesson can be solved with one step. You can use the Properties of Equality and inverse operations to isolate the variable. What operation is the inverse of multiplication?

WORKED EXAMPLE

Solve the equation $4r = 32$.

$$4r = 32$$

$$4(1r) = 4(8)$$ Write equivalent expressions with similar structure.

$$\frac{4(1r)}{4} = \frac{4(8)}{4}$$ Use inverse operations to reverse the multiplication of 4 and $1r$.

$$1r = 1(8)$$ Perform division.

$$r = 8$$ Identity Property of Multiplication

The Identity Property of Multiplication states that for any number m, $m \cdot 1 = m$. In other words, when you multiply by 1, the number stays the same.

1. Examine the worked example.

   a. Check the solution to $4r = 32$.

   b. Are there other solutions to the equation? How do you know?

2. Use the same strategy to solve each equation.

   a. $8a = 72$

   b. $11t = 132$

LESSON 3: Play It In Reverse • M3-127

When you worked with one-step addition equations, you used the Subtraction Property of Equality to more efficiently solve the problem. Similarly, you can use the Division Property of Equality to solve multiplication problems.

3. Write the properties that justify each step.

$$6w = 90$$

$$\frac{6w}{6} = \frac{90}{6} \qquad \rule{6cm}{0.4pt}$$

$$1w = 15 \qquad \rule{6cm}{0.4pt}$$

$$w = 15 \qquad \rule{6cm}{0.4pt}$$

4. Diego and Venita are solving the equation $5 = \frac{p}{7}$.

   a. Diego says that to solve $5 = \frac{p}{7}$, he would divide by 7. The value of p that makes the equation true is $\frac{5}{7}$. Venita disagrees and says that they should divide by $\frac{1}{7}$, and the solution is 35. Who is correct?

   b. How can Diego and Venita check to see whose answer is correct?

5. Compare the solution strategies used by Sydney and Kailey. What do you notice?

Sydney

$\frac{2}{5}x = 20$

$\dfrac{\frac{2}{5}x}{\frac{2}{5}} = \dfrac{20}{\frac{2}{5}}$

$1x = 20\left(\frac{5}{2}\right)$

$x = 50$

Kailey

$\frac{2}{5}x = 20$

$\left(\frac{5}{2}\right)\frac{2}{5}x = \left(\frac{5}{2}\right)20$

$1x = 50$

$x = 50$

6. Solve each equation. Check to ensure that your solution makes the original equation a true statement.

a. $\frac{n}{4} = 7$

b. $18 = 3y$

c. $\frac{3}{2}h = \frac{5}{2}$

d. $3.14s = 81.2004$

e. $3\frac{1}{3} = \frac{3}{10}w$

f. $4.2k = 14.7$

ACTIVITY	Reasoning About More
3.5	**Interesting Multiplication Equations**

Recall that an equation is created by writing two expressions with an equals sign between them. Equations can be sometimes, always, or never true.

Consider the equation $7c = 28d$.

1. How is this equation different from the equations you have solved in this lesson?

2. Generate at least 3 pairs of values for c and d that make the equation true.

3. What patterns do you notice?

Using number sense to rewrite equivalent expressions to solve equations is a valid strategy.

You can use properties of arithmetic and algebra, along with the properties of equality, to solve for one of the variables in terms of the other variable.

> ### WORKED EXAMPLE
>
> $$12a = 84b$$
> Step 1 $12a = (12 \cdot 7)b$
> Step 2 $12a = 12(7b)$
> Step 3 $a = 7b$

4. Analyze the worked example.

   a. Why was 84 decomposed into $12 \cdot 7$?

b. What property was applied in Step 2?

c. Explain the reasoning from Step 2 to Step 3. Which property was used?

5. Jesse and Dominic each proposed a solution for the equation $7c = 28d$. Who's correct?

Jesse	Dominic
$7c = 28d$	$7c = 28d$
$7c = (7 \cdot 4)d$	$\left(\frac{4}{4}\right)7c = 28d$
$7c = 7(4d)$	$\frac{(4 \cdot 7)c}{4} = 28d$
$c = 4d$	$28\left(\frac{c}{4}\right) = 28d$
	$\frac{c}{4} = d$

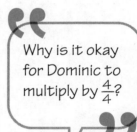

Why is it okay for Dominic to multiply by $\frac{4}{4}$?

Use reasoning to solve each equation for one of the variables.

6. $18m = 54n$

7. $12s = \frac{1}{2}t$

TALK the TALK 💬

What's Your Strategy?

Each equation in this lesson is written as $px = q$, where p and q are positive rational numbers and x is the unknown. You have investigated different strategies to solve these equations.

Analyze each given equation.
- Do you recognize a fact family relationship between the numerical coefficient and the constant?
- Is the numerical coefficient a whole number? A fraction? Or a decimal?
- Do you recognize a way to form a numerical coefficient of 1 using a Property of Equality?

$2n = 12$ $\frac{2}{5}x = 14$ $3x = 55$ $1.1m = 5.5$

$1.45r = 5.9$ $7h = 35$ $\frac{x}{4} = \frac{3}{8}$ $8r = \frac{3}{4}$

1. Sort each equation according to the solution strategy you think is most efficient.

Use Number Sense to Write Equivalent Expressions	Division Property of Equality	Multiplication Property of Equality

2. Provide a rationale for your choice of solution strategy or strategies.

Assignment

Write

Explain how to solve the equation $px = q$ for x. Be sure to include the properties you use in the process.

Remember

A solution to an equation is the value or values for the variable that makes the equation true. To solve a one-step multiplication equation, isolate the variable using number sense, the Division Property of Equality, or the Multiplication Property of Equality.

Practice

1. Solve each equation using a bar model.

   a. $3x = 10$

   b. $\frac{x}{5} = 6$

   c. $\frac{3}{5}x = 12$

   d. $\frac{5}{4}x = \frac{2}{3}$

2. Solve each equation. Check your solutions.

   a. $2.1 = 0.5y$

   b. $4r = 26$

   c. $\frac{2}{9}h = 8$

   d. $\frac{4}{3} = \frac{8}{3}b$

   e. $14 = \frac{s}{3}$

   f. $3.8x = 2.736$

3. Bertrand invites 21 people to his party and wants to give each guest 3 party favors. If n is the total number of party favors he will need to order, the equation that represents this situation is $\frac{n}{21} = 3$.

   a. If Bertrand orders 58 party favors, will he be able to give each guest 3 party favors? That is, is 58 a solution to the equation?

   b. If Bertrand orders 62 party favors, will he be able to give each guest 3 party favors?

   c. How many party favors does Bertrand need to order? Use the equation to determine the solution. State the inverse operation needed to isolate the variable. Then, solve the equation. Check your solution.

Stretch

Like bar models, balances are also used to model equation solving. Consider the balances shown.

A

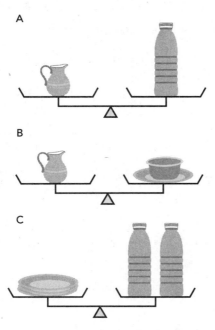

B

C

On balance A, a water pitcher balances with a juice bottle. On balance B, the water pitcher balances a cereal bowl and plate. On balance C, three plates balance two juice bottles. How many cereal bowls will balance a water pitcher?

Review

Solve each equation. Check your solutions.

1. $2.6 + j = 7.1$

2. $\frac{21}{5} = b + \frac{3}{4}$

Rewrite each expression as the product of a constant and a sum of terms.

3. $2x + 5$

4. $\frac{1}{2}x + \frac{3}{5}$

Determine the conversion.

5. 6 inches = _____ centimeters

6. 10 kilometers = _____ miles

Getting Real

Solving Equations to Solve Problems

4

WARM UP

Determine each quotient using long division.

1. $435 \div 25$

2. $511 \div 30$

3. $860 \div 23$

LEARNING GOALS

- Use variables to represent quantities in expressions describing real-world values.
- Solve problems by writing and solving equations.
- Interpret remainders in division problems.

KEY TERM

- literal equation

You know about expressions and equations and how they often represent the structure of real-world situations. How can you apply your knowledge to write equations and solve real-world and mathematical problems?

Equations, Literally

You have already learned a lot of important equations in mathematics. Some of these equations are literal equations. **Literal equations** are equations in which the variables represent specific measures. You most often see literal equations when you study formulas.

For example, the formula for the area of a triangle, $A = \frac{1}{2}bh$, is a literal equation. The variables in this equation represent the measures of the area, base, and height of the triangle.

1. **Consider the formula for area of a parallelogram.**

   a. **Write the formula for area, A, use b to represent the base and h to represent the height.**

   b. **Solve the equation for b.**

   c. **Solve the equation for h.**

2. **The total cost, t, of an online order is the cost of the items, c, plus the cost of shipping, s.**

   a. **Write an equation to represent the total cost.**

   b. **Solve the equation for the cost of the items.**

   c. **Solve the equation for the cost of shipping.**

3. **You can calculate the distance, d, of an object traveling at a constant rate by multiplying the rate, r, by the time, t. Write an equation in terms of each quantity.**

   a. **distance**　　　　b. **rate**　　　　c. **time**

ACTIVITY 4.1

Using Equations to Solve Problems

Write and solve an equation for each problem. Show your work and label your answers. Describe the strategy you used to determine each solution.

1. Raul's sister is 6 years older than he is. What is Raul's age if Raul's sister is 19 years old?

2. Approximately $\frac{1}{10}$ of the mass of a medium-sized apple is sugar. What is the approximate mass of a medium-sized apple that contains 19 grams of sugar?

3. Oscar made brownies for his class. He tripled the recipe he normally uses. If he made 36 brownies for his class, how many brownies does his original recipe make?

4. In June of 2016, for every 20 total emails a person received, they could expect to get 11 spam emails. If a person received 300 spam emails in one month, how many total emails did they receive?

5. In Jaden's town, the middle school has 443 more students than the high school. If the middle school has 817 students, how many students are at the high school?

6. The average height of an ostrich, the tallest bird, is 121 inches. The average height of a bee hummingbird, the smallest bird, is 2.75 inches. How many times taller is the ostrich than the bee hummingbird?

ACTIVITY 4.2

Problems and Puzzles

For each question, write an equation to represent the situation and then solve it to answer the equation. A situation may require more than one equation.

1. Kendra bought some back-to-school supplies for $1.70. She showed them to her friend Naya: 2 erasers for 2 cents each, 5 markers for 4 cents each. She also bought 8 notepads, but she forgot how much she paid for them. She did not pay sales tax.

   Naya said that she was not charged the right amount. How did she know?

2. The Bermuda Triangle is an imaginary triangle connecting Miami, Florida, to San Juan, Puerto Rico, to Bermuda. The Bermuda Triangle covers an area of 454,000 square miles. The dashed line on the map shows a distance of about 926 miles.

   What is the approximate distance from Bermuda to Puerto Rico?

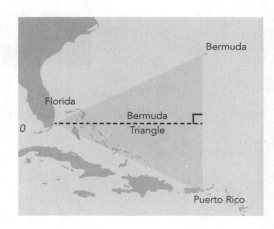

3. Amit's school is an unusual school. It has 1677 students in grades 3–6. There are twice as many fifth graders as sixth graders and three times as many fourth graders as fifth graders. Finally, there are five times as many third graders as fourth graders. How many fifth graders are in Amit's school?

4. There are two routes Jasmine can take when she bikes home from school—the long way and the short way. The long way is $1\frac{1}{2}$ times as far as the short way. During one week, she biked a total of 30 miles from school to home. She took the short way three times.

a. What is the distance of the short way?

b. What is the distance of the long way?

Interpreting Remainders in Solutions

1. The Red Cross disaster relief fund collected 3551 winter coats to distribute to flood victims. If there are 23 distribution centers, how many coats can be sent to each center? Marla's calculations are shown.

Marla said, "The Red Cross can send $154\frac{9}{23}$ coats to each center." Madison replied, "You cannot have a fraction of a coat. So, each center will receive 154 coats and there will be 9 coats left over."

Who's correct and why?

$$
\begin{array}{r}
154\frac{9}{23} \\
23\overline{)3551} \\
-23 \\
\hline
125 \\
-115 \\
\hline
101 \\
-92 \\
\hline
9
\end{array}
$$

In division problems, the remainder can mean different things in different situations. Sometimes the remainder can be ignored, and sometimes the remainder is the answer to the problem. Sometimes the answer is the number without the remainder, and sometimes you need to use the next whole number up from the correct answer.

> In other words, you can round down if you don't need to use the remainder, and you can round up if you need the next whole number larger than your answer.

2. The Carnegie Middle School is hosting a picnic for any fifth grader who will be attending school next year as a sixth grader. The hospitality committee is planning the picnic for 125 students. Each fifth grader will get a sandwich, a drink, and a dessert.

a. The hospitality committee is ordering large sandwiches that each serve 8 people. If 125 fifth graders are coming to the picnic, how many sandwiches should the committee buy?

b. The committee is planning to have frozen fruit bars for dessert. If frozen fruit bars come in boxes of 12, how many boxes of frozen fruit bars should they order?

c. They will be serving bottles of water. Bottled water comes in cases of 24. How many cases of water will they need? Will there be any extra bottles of water? If so, how many?

d. The fifth graders will take a bus from the elementary school to the middle school on the afternoon of the picnic. If each bus seats 32 passengers, how many buses will be needed to transport the students? How many seats will be empty?

3. Throughout the year, local businesses collected 28,654 pairs of eyeglasses for disaster victims. If they have requests from 236 relief organizations, how many pairs of eyeglasses can each organization receive? How many pairs, if any, will be left over?

TALK the TALK

Write Your Own

1. Write your own word problem that can be solved by writing and solving the equation $2.4 + x = 5$.

2. Write your own word problem that can be solved by writing and solving the equation $4x = 8$.

Assignment

Write

Write a definition of *literal equation* in your own words.

Remember

In division problems, the remainder can mean different things in different situations. Sometimes the remainder can be ignored, and sometimes the remainder is the answer to the problem. Sometimes the answer is the quotient without the remainder, and sometimes you need to use the next whole number up from the quotient.

Practice

1. Solve each equation. Show your work.
   a. $3y = 18$
   b. $m + 12 = 29$
   c. $3g = 6.3$
   d. $5x = 12 + 18$
   e. $2(a + 2a) = 90$

For each problem, write an equation to represent the situation and then solve it to answer the question.

2. A rectangular pool has a width of 24 feet. A second rectangular pool has a perimeter of 48 feet, which is $\frac{1}{3}$ the perimeter of the first pool.

3. The local firefighters collect toys to distribute at various give-away events. They have 4569 toys and will sponsor 129 give-away events. How many toys can they give away at each event? How many toys, if any, will be left over?

Stretch

You read a report that says that only $\frac{7}{100}$ of all people who own car dealerships in the country are women.

1. There are about 20,000 people who own car dealerships in the country. How many of them are female?
2. In a group of 2000 people who own car dealerships attending a conference, about how many would you expect to be female?
3. How did you determine the number of women car dealers, given the total number of car dealers? Use complete sentences to explain your answer.
4. Write an expression to represent the number of women car dealers, given the total number of car dealers.
5. Write an equation that you can use to determine the total number of car dealers in a certain city, given that the number of women car dealers in the city is 14.
6. Use the equation to determine the total number of car dealers in the city.

Review

1. Rewrite each algebraic expression by applying the Distributive Property.

   a. $3.5(2x + 1)$

   b. $\frac{1}{2}(3 - 4a)$

2. Create a bar model to solve each equation.

   a. $4x = 30$

   b. $\frac{3}{5}x = 21$

3. Write a different division problem that has the same quotient as the one given. Explain your answer.

   a. $36.5 \div 0.005$ b. $63.196 \div 14.8$

Equations Summary

KEY TERMS

- equation
- Reflexive Property of Equality
- solution
- Addition Property of Equality
- Subtraction Property of Equality
- Multiplication Property of Equality
- Division Property of Equality
- Symmetric Property of Equality
- Zero Property of Multiplication
- Identity Property of Multiplication
- Identity Property of Addition
- graph of an inequality
- solution set of an inequality
- bar model
- one-step equation
- inverse operations
- literal equation

LESSON 1

First Among Equals

An **equation** is a statement of equality between two expressions. An equation can contain numbers, variables, or both in the same mathematical sentence. Equations may be always true, never true, or true only for one or more values of the variable. The **Reflexive Property of Equality** says that when both sides of an equation look exactly the same, their values are equal.

A **solution** to an equation is any value for the variable that makes the equation true.

Properties of Equality are logical rules that allow you to maintain balance and rewrite equations.

Always True	Never True	True for certain values of the variable
$6 = 10 - 4$	$10 = 20$	$x = 5$
$x = x$	$x = x + 2$	$x + 2 = 12$

Properties of Equality	For all numbers a, b, and c
Addition Property of Equality	If $a = b$, then $a + c = b + c$.
Subtraction Property of Equality	If $a = b$, then $a - c = b - c$.
Multiplication Property of Equality	If $a = b$, then $a \cdot c = b \cdot c$.
Division Property of Equality	If $a = b$ and $c \neq 0$, then $\frac{a}{c} = \frac{b}{c}$.
Symmetric Property of Equality	If $a = b$, then $b = a$.

Equations that have an infinite number of solutions are equations that are true regardless of the value you assign to the variable. These kinds of equations often describe important properties of numbers. For example:

- The **Zero Property of Multiplication** states that the product of any number and 0 is 0: $x \cdot 0 = 0$.
- The **Identity Property of Multiplication** states that the product of any number and 1 is the number: $x \cdot 1 = x$.
- The **Identity Property of Addition** states that the sum of any number and 0 is the number: $x + 0 = x$.

You can use a number line to represent inequalities. **The graph of an inequality** in one variable is the set of all points on a number line that make the inequality true. The set of all points that make an inequality true is the **solution set of the inequality**.

The solution to any inequality can be represented on a number line by a ray. A ray begins at a starting point and goes on forever in one direction. A closed circle means that the starting point is part of the solution set of the inequality. An open circle means that the starting point is not part of the solution set of the inequality.

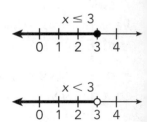

For example, the solution set of the inequality $x \leq 3$ is all numbers equal to or less than 3, and the solution set of the inequality $x < 3$ is all numbers less than 3.

LESSON
2

Bar None

A **bar model** uses rectangular bars to represent known and unknown quantities.

For example, the equation $x + 10 = 15$ states that for some value of x, the expression $x + 10$ is equal to 15. This can be represented using a bar model.

x + 10

15

The expression $x + 10$ can be decomposed into a part representing x and a part representing 10. The number 15 can be decomposed in a similar way: $15 = 5 + 10$. The bar model demonstrates that these two equations are equivalent.

x	10

x + 10

15

5	10

$$x + 10 = 15$$
$$x + 10 = 5 + 10$$

By examining the structure of the second equation, you can see that 5 is the value for x that makes this equation true.

A **one-step equation** is an equation that can be solved using only one operation. To solve a one-step addition equation, isolate the variable using number sense or inverse operations. **Inverse operations** are pairs of operations that reverse the effects of each other.

For example, solve the equation $h + 6 = 19$.

$h + 6 = 13 + 6$ Write equivalent expressions that mirror structure.

$h + 6 - 6 = 13 + 6 - 6$ Use inverse operations to reverse the addition of 6 to h.

$h + 0 = 13 + 0$ Combine like terms and apply the Additive Identity Property.

$h = 13$

Play It In Reverse

You can also use bar models to reason about the solution to multiplication equations.

For example, the equation $2x = 6$ states that for some value of x, the expression $2x$ is equal to 6. You can decompose $2x$ by rewriting it as the equivalent expression $1x + 1x$, or $x + x$. To maintain equivalence, decompose 6 in a similar way. The bar model demonstrates that these two equations are equivalent.

$$2x = 6$$
$$x + x = 3 + 3$$

2x

6

x	x

2x

6

3	3

By examining the structure of the second equation, you can see that $x = 3$.

Bar models can also be used to solve multiplication equations with fractional coefficients.

For example, represent $\frac{1}{3}x = 2$ as a bar model.

$\frac{1}{3}x$

2

To solve this equation for x, compose 3 equally-sized parts to create the whole, x. To maintain equivalence, compose 3 equally-sized parts for the other expression too. This structure allows you to see the value of x that makes the equation true: $x = 6$.

x

$\frac{1}{3}x$	$\frac{1}{3}x$	$\frac{1}{3}x$

2	2	2

6

You can also use the inverse operation of multiplication to solve one-step multiplication equations.

For example, solve the equation $4r = 32$.

$$4r = 32$$

$4(1r) = 4(8)$ Write equivalent expressions with similar structure.

$\dfrac{4(1r)}{4} = \dfrac{4(8)}{4}$ Use inverse operations to reverse the multiplication of 4 and $1r$.

$1r = 1(8)$ Perform division.

$r = 8$ Identity Property of Multiplication

You can use properties of arithmetic and algebra, along with the properties of equality, to solve for one of the variables in an equation in terms of the other variable.

$$12a = 84b$$

Step 1 $12a = (12 \cdot 7)b$

Step 2 $12a = 12(7b)$

Step 3 $a = 7b$

<table>
<tr><td>LESSON
4</td><td>Getting Real</td></tr>
</table>

Literal equations are equations in which the variables represent specific measures. You most often see literal equations when you study formulas. The formula for the area of a triangle, $A = \frac{1}{2}bh$, is a literal equation. The variables represent the measures of the base and height of the triangle.

In division problems, the remainder can mean different things in different situations. Sometimes the remainder can be ignored, and sometimes the remainder is the answer to the problem. Sometimes the answer is the quotient without the remainder, and sometimes you need to use the next whole number up from the quotient.

For example, the Red Cross disaster relief fund collected 4233 winter coats to distribute to flood victims. If there are 28 distribution centers, how many coats can be sent to each center?

$$4233 \div 28 = 151\frac{5}{28}$$

You cannot have a fraction of a coat, so each center will receive 151 coats and there will be 5 coats left over.

Graphing Quantitative Relationships

On a long run, runners keep track of their splits. For example, on a half-marathon (13.1-mile run), the runner's time is measured at 5 miles, 10 miles, and at the finish line.

Module 3: Determining Unknown Quantities

TOPIC 3: GRAPHING QUANTITATIVE RELATIONSHIPS

Students learn that quantities can vary in relation to each other and are often classified as independent and dependent quantities. They solve for unknown values of a variable by analyzing a graph. Students then solve linear equations using the variety of tools available to them, and they contrast the advantages and limitations of each. Throughout the topic, students compare and contrast linear equations of the form $y = x + c$ and $y = cx$, and their respective representations. Finally, they analyze three different distance, rate, and time scenarios and generalize the formula $d = rt$. Students are expected to use their knowledge of unit rate and unit conversion to solve these problems.

Where have we been?

In grade 5 as well as in previous topics, students graphed and named ordered pairs in the first quadrant of the coordinate plane. This topic begins by asking students to interpret graphs located only in Quadrant I. It also connects to graphs of equivalent ratios and writing inequalities as constraints, which students learned about in previous lessons.

Where are we going?

This topic provides the foundation for the formal study of independent and dependent variables, which will be revisited later in this course. In Module 4 and then in grade 7, students will continue analyzing different representations of scenarios, but they will no longer be restricted to Quadrant I. This topic also combats a common misconception – that all relationships between variables are linear – by exposing students to nonlinear graphs and scenarios.

Using a Graph to Visualize an Equation

In this example, the graph models the expression $1.25x$, where x is the number of pretzels sold, and $1.25x$ is the amount of money collected. This graph intersects a horizontal line which represents the expression 10. The x-coordinate of the point at which the lines intersect represents the solution to the equation $10 = 1.25x$, so $x = 8$.

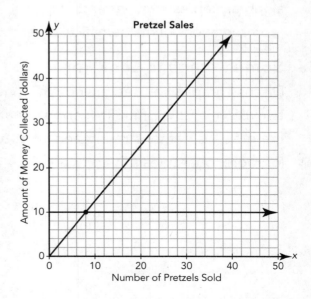

Myth: Memory is like an audio or video recording.

Let's play a game. Memorize the following list of words: *strawberry, grape, watermelon, banana, orange, peach, cherry, blueberry, raspberry*. Got it? Good. Some believe that the brain stores memories in pristine form. The idea is that memories last for a long time and don't change – like recordings. Without looking back at the original list, was *apple* on it?

If you answered "*yes,*" then go back and look at the list. You'll see that *apple* does not appear, even though it seems like it should. In other words, memory is an active, reconstructive process that takes additional information, like the category of words (e.g., fruit), and makes assumptions about the stored information.

This simple demonstration suggests memory is *not* like a recording. Instead, it is influenced by prior knowledge and decays over time. Therefore, students need to see and engage with the same information multiple times to minimize forgetting (and distortions).

#mathmythbusted

Talking Points

You can further support your student's learning by asking questions about the work they do in class or at home. Your student is learning to make connections between algebraic representations and graphical representations of mathematical objects.

Some Things to Look For

Discuss graphs you see online, on television, and in print. Talk about what the graph is demonstrating and what two (or more) quantities it is comparing.

Key Terms

discrete graph
A discrete gragh is a graph of isolated points.

continuous graph
A continuous graph is a graph with no breaks in it; each point on it represents a solution to the graphed scenario.

dependent quantity
When one quantity depends on another in a problem situation, it is said to be the dependent quantity.

independent quantity
The quantity on which the dependent quantity depends is called the independent quantity.

Every Graph Tells a Story

Independent and Dependent Variables

WARM UP

Write an inequality for each verbal statement.

1. x is less than 5.

2. 4 times g is no more than 9.

3. y is at least 2 more than x.

4. 3 less than the product of 4 and some number is greater than another number.

LEARNING GOALS

- Interpret information about a situation from a graphical representation.
- Determine whether graphs are discrete or continuous.
- Identify the graphs of situations.
- Identify and use variables to define independent and dependent quantities in real-world problems.
- Write an equation to express a quantity that is the dependent variable in terms of another quantity, the independent variable.

KEY TERMS

- discrete graph
- continuous graph
- dependent quantity
- independent quantity
- independent variable
- dependent variable

Throughout this course, you have analyzed quantities in a variety of ways. Often, the equation you write to represent variable quantities depends on the question you are answering. How do you tell what variable quantity is the focus of a mathematical question?

It's Not a Tall Tale!

Write a story to describe the situation represented by each graph.

1. The Water Level in the Bathtub

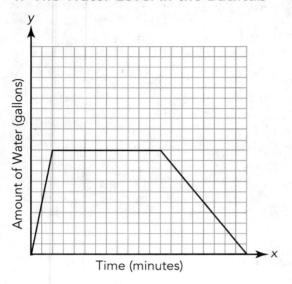

2. Money in Your Bank Account

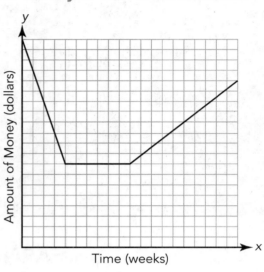

_____

_____

_____

_____

_____

_____

_____

_____

_____

_____

_____

_____

_____

_____

_____

_____

Match and Analyze

In this activity, you will match a specific graph to a real-world problem situation.

Cut out the graphs and scenarios located at the end of the lesson.

1. **Tape each graph in the box with the appropriate scenario. Label the axes with appropriate quantities and units.**

2. **How did you determine which graph matched which scenario?**

Even though only certain points make sense in the situation, you can draw a line to represent the shape of discrete data.

A **discrete graph** is a graph of isolated points. Often, the coordinates of those points are counting numbers. A **continuous graph** is a graph with no breaks in it. Each point on a continuous graph, even those with fractional numbers as coordinates, represents a solution to the graphed scenario.

3. Which graphs are discrete graphs and which are continuous graphs? How does the scenario inform you that the graph will display discrete points or be continuous?

4. Which graph(s) represent equivalent ratios? How does the scenario inform you that the graph(s) will display equivalent ratios?

5. Consider the graph in the Rainy Day scenario. Assume that 2 hours after you left home, 1.5 inches of rain had fallen.

   a. Explain how the graph illustrates that the rain fell faster later in the day than at the beginning of the day.

   b. Write an inequality statement in terms of the time, t, to represent when the rain stopped for the day.

6. Consider the graph in the Toy Rocket scenario. The rocket reaches a maximum height of 256 feet.

   a. Describe the shape of the graph.

   b. Write an inequality statement in terms of the time, t, to represent when the rocket was rising into the air.

7. Consider the graph of the T-shirt Sales scenario. Suppose there is a minimum order total of $100 when you are ordering the T-shirts. Write an inequality statement for the number of shirts, n, that must be ordered to meet the minimum order requirement.

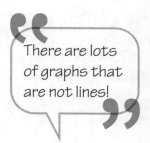

There are lots of graphs that are not lines!

Be sure to keep your graphs and scenarios. You will use them in the next activity.

ACTIVITY 1.2

Quantities That Change

When one quantity depends on another in a real-world problem situation, it is said to be the **dependent quantity**. The quantity on which it depends is called the **independent quantity**. The variable that represents the independent quantity is called the **independent variable**, and the variable that represents the dependent quantity is called the **dependent variable**.

Consider the scenarios from the previous activity.

1. Use the Pool Party scenario to answer each question.

   a. What two quantities are changing in this situation?

   b. Which quantity depends on the other?

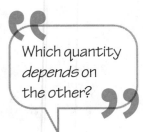

Which quantity *depends* on the other?

   c. Define variables for each quantity and label them appropriately as the independent and dependent variables.

2. Use the Fish Tank scenario to answer each question.

   a. What two quantities are changing in this situation?

   b. Which quantity is the independent quantity and which is the dependent quantity?

c. The equation that represents the fish scenario is
$w = 200 - 10t$. What do the variables w and t
represent in this equation?

d. What do you notice about which variable is isolated in
the equation?

3. Identify the independent quantity and the dependent quantity
in each of the four remaining scenarios.

a. Rainy Day

   Independent Quantity:

   Dependent Quantity:

Examine the
graphs. Do
you see any
connection
between the
independent
and dependent
variables and
the graph?

b. Toy Rocket

   Independent Quantity:

   Dependent Quantity:

c. DVD and Game Rentals

   Independent Quantity:

   Dependent Quantity:

d. T-shirt Sales

   Independent Quantity:

   Dependent Quantity:

Total Price and Profit

Profit is the extra money for selling items, over and above the cost of producing the items.

A store makes 20% profit on the total price of all the items they sell.

Analyze the situation.

1. **Name the two quantities that are changing.**

2. **Describe which value depends on the other.**

Let t represent the total price of all items sold in dollars, and let p represent the profit in dollars.

3. **Write an equation to represent the relationship between these variables.**

4. **Identify the independent and dependent variables in this situation.**

5. Complete the table.

	Independent Quantity	Dependent Quantity
Quantity Name		
Unit of Measure		
Variable		
	25.00	
	49.95	
	99.95	

6. Use the table to complete the graph.

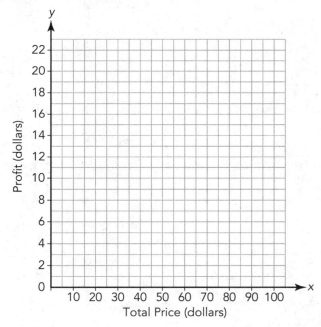

7. Is this a discrete graph or a continuous graph? Explain.

8. On which axis is the independent variable? On which axis is the dependent variable?

Why do you think the axes are labeled with total price on the horizontal axis and profit on the vertical axis?

ACTIVITY 1.4   Profit and Total Price

Let's think about the problem situation in a different way.

Suppose you are operating this store and you know how much profit you make on each item.

1. Name the two quantities that are changing.

2. Describe which value depends on the other.

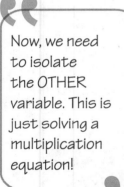

> Now, we need to isolate the OTHER variable. This is just solving a multiplication equation!

Let p be equal to the profit, and let t be equal to the total price of all items sold.

3. Write an equation to represent the relationship between these variables.

4. Identify the independent and dependent variables in this situation.

5. Complete the table.

	Independent Quantity	Dependent Quantity
Quantity Name		
Unit of Measure		
Variable		
	7.50	
	10.00	
	19.99	

6. Use the table to complete the graph.

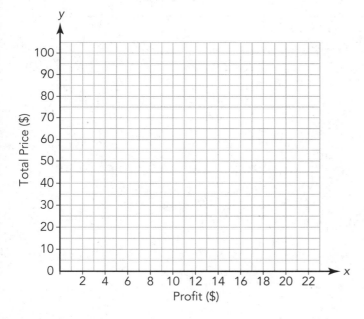

Why are the labels on your axes different from the previous graph?

7. Is this a discrete graph or a continuous graph? Explain.

8. On which axis is the independent variable? On which axis is the dependent variable?

The situations in the previous activities, *Total Price and Profit* and *Profit and Total Price*, are similar but presented in two different ways.

1. Complete each summary statement.

Total Price and Profit
The _____ depends on the _____.   Equation:

Profit and Total Price
The _____ depends on the _____.   Equation:

> It's important to determine the goal of the problem before you start working.

2. What do you notice about the two equations?

3. How does examining this same situation from different perspectives affect the independent and dependent variables?

4. What can you conclude about the designation of a variable as independent or dependent?

5. Compare the two graphs in the activities *Total Price and Profit* and *Profit and Total Price*.

   a. How are they similar and how are they different?

   b. What do you notice about the independent and dependent variables?

Consider another scenario.

Dawson purchased a diesel-powered car that averages 41 miles per gallon.

6. Suppose Dawson is interested in how far the car travels on a given amount of gas.

   a. Identify the independent and dependent quantities.

   b. Define variables for each quantity and identify which is the independent variable and which is the dependent variable.

   c. Write an equation to represent the relationship between the two variables.

7. Suppose, instead, that Dawson runs out of gas on a regular basis. He is interested in how many gallons of gas he has used if he knows how many miles he has driven. Use the same variables you defined in Question 6.

   a. Identify which variable represents the independent quantity and which variable represents the dependent quantity.

   b. Write an equation to represent the relationship between the two variables.

8. How would you expect the graphs of the two situations to be similar? How would they be different?

TALK the TALK

Create Your Own Story

1. Create a real-world situation to match the given graph.

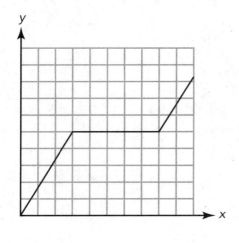

_____

_____

_____

_____

_____

_____

2. Identify the independent and dependent quantities
   in your scenario.

3. Label the x-axis and y-axis to reflect your scenario.

4. What real-world question could be answered using the graph based on your scenario.

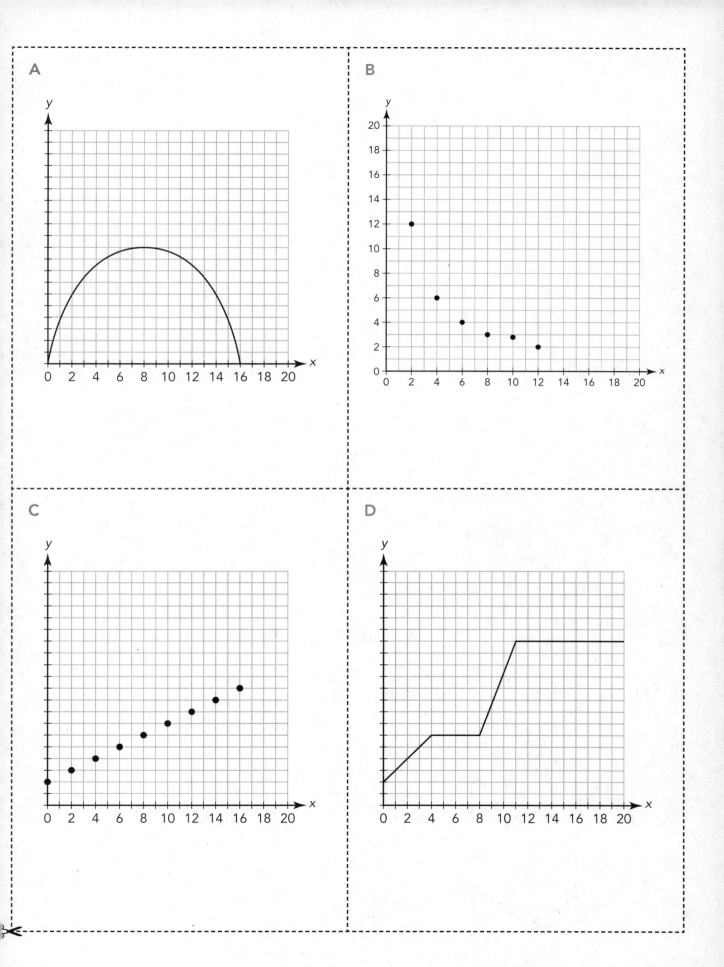

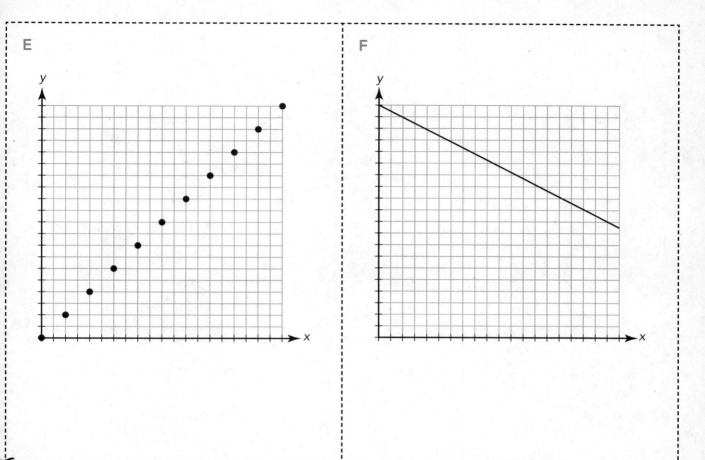

E

F

Pool Party

You have cookies for your team pool party, but you don't know how many of your teammates will show up.
How many cookies will each teammate receive if everyone receives the same number of cookies?

Fish Tank

You are draining a 200-gallon fish tank at a rate of 10 gallons per minute. How much water remains in the tank at a specific time?

Rainy Day

When you left home, the rain was falling at a steady rate. Then, it stopped raining for a few hours before a sudden downpour. Finally, it stopped raining. How many inches of rain had fallen at different points of the day?

Toy Rocket

You launch a toy rocket into the air from the ground and observe its height through its entire flight. How many feet high was the rocket at a specific time after launch?

DVD and Game Rentals

The video kiosk charges $2.00 for DVD and game rentals. How many DVDs and games can you rent for different amounts of money?

T-shirt Sales

You buy T-shirts to sell for your school. There is a $25 design charge plus the cost per T-shirt. What is the total cost for different numbers of T-shirts?

Assignment

Write

Write the term that best completes each statement.

1. In a real-world problem situation, when a quantity does not depend on another quantity, it is called the _____. In the equation that models the problem situation, this quantity is represented by the _____.

2. In a real-world problem situation, when a quantity depends on another quantity, it is called the _____. In the equation that models the problem situation, this quantity is represented by the _____.

Remember

The mathematical or real-world question asked often determines which quantity depends on the other. When graphed, the independent quantity is plotted on the horizontal axis and the dependent quantity is plotted on the vertical axis.

Practice

1. Determine the independent variable and the dependent variable in each given equation.
   a. The equation $T = 75 - d$ is used to calculate the water temperature, T, at a depth, d, in a particular lake.
   b. The equation $p = \frac{t}{3}$ is used to calculate the individual profit, p, made by each of three brothers operating a lemonade stand with a total profit, t.

2. An online ticket broker charges a flat service fee of $6.50 per ticket sold. You are interested in the total amount of money you must pay for a given number of tickets.
   a. Name the two quantities that are changing in this situation.
   b. Define variables for each quantity and identify which represents the independent quantity and which represents the dependent quantity.
   c. Write an equation for the relationship between the two variables.

3. Jana is a runner. When she is training for a race, she averages 8 miles per hour. She is interested in how far she can run in a given number of hours.
   a. Define variables for each changing quantity and identify each as the independent or dependent variable.
   b. Write an equation to represent this situation.
   c. Use your equation to create a table of values for this situation.
   d. Use your equation and table to create a graph. Remember to label your axes.
   e. Explain how you knew which variable to graph on each axis.
   f. Rewrite the equation from part (b) with the other variable isolated.
   g. With the equation in this form, which variable is the independent and which is the dependent? Explain your reasoning.
   h. Write a question for which the equation in (f) would be needed.

Stretch

Create two different scenarios that use time as a varying quantity. In one scenario, use time as the independent quantity. In the other, use time as the dependent quantity. Write a question that could be answered in each case. Create a graph for each situation.

Review

1. When Sarah goes out to eat, she always tips her server 18% of the bill. She also must pay 7% sales tax on her dinner.
   a. Define variables for the quantities in the situation.
   b. Write an equation for the total cost of Sarah's meal, including tax and tip.
   c. Suppose Sarah paid a total of $31.25. How much was her meal?

2. A builder requires a certain number of bricks each time he builds a brick structure. To make sure he has enough bricks, he always orders 50 additional bricks.
   a. Define variables for the quantities in the situation.
   b. Write an equation for the total number of bricks ordered.
   c. Suppose the builder calculated that the needed 1275 bricks. How many bricks were ordered?

3. Solve each equation and state the inverse operation you used.
   a. $t + 4\frac{3}{4} = 8$
   b. $22 = \frac{11}{7}y$

4. Write the two possible unit rates for each ratio.
   a. 8 cups of sugar for every 2 tablespoons of vanilla
   b. $3.56 for 24 ounces

The Power of the Horizontal Line

Using Graphs to Solve One-Step Equations

WARM UP

Which equations represent proportional relationships? Explain how you know.

1. $c = 2.5n$

2. $l = w + 25$

3. $d = \frac{1}{3}t$

4. $T = 100 - d$

LEARNING GOALS

- Analyze the relationship between the independent and dependent variables in a graph and relate the variables to an equation.
- Use multiple representations to solve one-step real-world problems.
- Use an inequality of the form $x > c$ or $x < c$ to represent constraints when solving a real-world problem.

You have learned how to solve one-step equations using reasoning and the Properties of Equality. How can you use graphs to solve one-step real-world problems?

> What are the independent and dependent quantities in this situation?

Selling Pretzels

Nic sells pretzels for $1.25 each at the morning baseball and softball games held at the Community Center. At the end of the games he is supposed to report the number of pretzels he sold and the total amount of money collected.

Nic sold pretzels on three different mornings, but he only reported either the number of pretzels sold or the dollar amount collected.

1. Calculate each missing piece of information from his daily reports.

   a. 16 pretzels sold

   b. 40 pretzels sold

   c. $40 collected

2. Write an equation to represent the relationship between the number of pretzels sold, x, and the amount of money collected in dollars, y.

3. Does this situation represent a proportional relationship? Justify your answer.

Using a Graph to Determine Unknown Quantities

In the previous activity, you answered questions and wrote the equation $y = 1.25x$, where x represents the number of pretzels sold and y represents the amount of money collected in dollars.

The amount of money collected for the number of pretzels sold can be represented by points on the graph. The graph shows the ordered pairs corresponding to the three questions you answered about Nic selling pretzels. The equation corresponding to the graph is $y = 1.25x$.

One way to analyze the relationship between ordered pairs displayed on a graph is to draw a line.

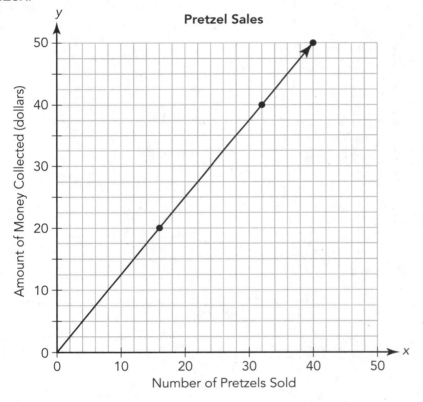

When you model a relationship with a line, it is up to you to consider each situation and interpret the meaning of the data values from the line drawn on a graph.

In some problem situations, when you draw a line all the points will make sense. In other problem situations, like this one, not all the points on the line will make sense.

1. Label the three ordered pairs shown on the graph.

2. What does each ordered pair represent?

3. Identify the unit rate in this situation. Plot and label it on the graph.

You can use a graph to determine an independent quantity given a dependent quantity.

WORKED EXAMPLE

You can use the graph to determine how many pretzels Nic sold if he collected $10.

First, locate 10 on the *y*-axis and draw a horizontal line. This shows that $10 is the amount of money collected. The *x*-value of the point where your horizontal line intersects with the graph of 1.25x is the number of pretzels sold for $10.

Remember, the solution to an equation is any value that makes the equation true. If you are given a graph, a solution is any point on that graph.

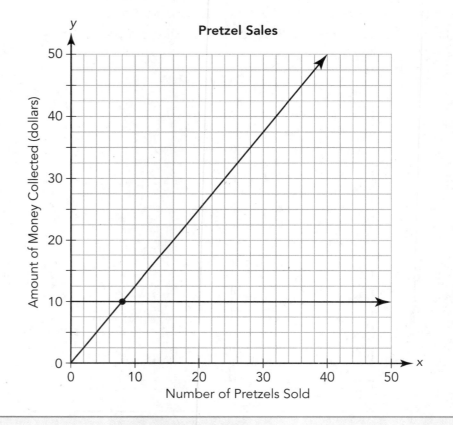

4. **How many pretzels did Nic sell if he collected $10?**

Use the graph in the worked example to answer each question.

5. How many pretzels did Nic sell if he collected:

   a. $25.00?

   b. $33.75?

   c. $75.00?

   d. more than $45.00?

   e. at least $100.00?

6. Nic reported that on Saturday morning he sold 13 pretzels and collected $16.25, and on Saturday afternoon he sold 42 pretzels and collected $55.00.

   Do you think he reported accurately? Explain your reasoning.

A flat fee is a one-time charge on each order, regardless of how many items are ordered.

An online site sells a single closeout item each day. The items and prices change daily. The company charges a flat fee of $6.00 for shipping.

The graph shown represents a model of this problem situation.

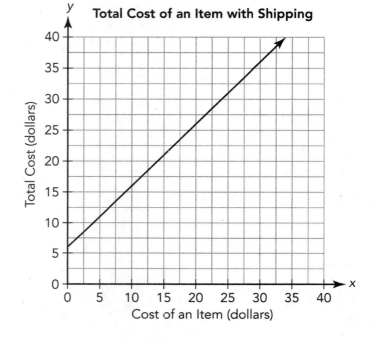

Total Cost of an Item with Shipping

In this problem situation, do all the points on the line make sense?

1. Write an equation to represent the relationship between the cost of an item, *x*, and the total cost, *y*. Label the graph of the line with your equation.

2. Does this situation represent a proportional relationship? Justify your answer.

Use the graph to answer each question.

3. What is the total cost if the cost of the item is:

   a. $18.00?   b. $25.00?

   c. $32.50?   d. $75.00?

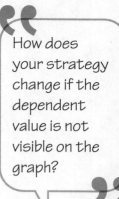

How does your strategy change if the dependent value is not visible on the graph?

4. Jeff was considering buying one of the daily closeout items that costs $23.99. He has a $25.00 gift card. Can he afford the total cost of the daily closeout item?

5. Suppose the flat fee for shipping changed to $6.80. How would the graph change? How would the equation change? Would that change the way you could use the graph to determine values?

6. How would the graph change if there was free shipping on all orders where the cost of the item is less than $20.00? Sketch the graph.

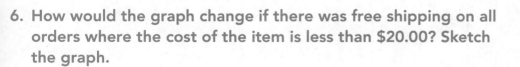

TALK the TALK

Plus or Times?

1. Describe the similarities and differences between the pairs of equations.

   a. $y = 5x$ and $y = x + 5$

   b. $y = \frac{1}{2}x$ and $y = \frac{1}{2} + x$

   c. $y = 4.95x$ and $y = x + 4.95$

2. Describe the similarities and differences among the graphs shown. Write an equation for each graph.

Graph A

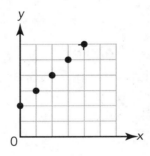

Graph B

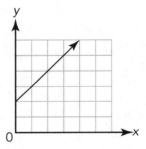

Graph C

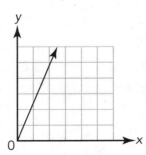

Graph D

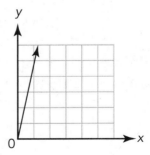

3. Describe how you can use a graph to solve one-step equations.

Assignment

Write

Describe the similarities and differences between the graphs of equations represented in the form $y = nx$ and $y = x + n$, where n is any positive rational number and x and y are unknown quantities.

Remember

Graphs are powerful visual representations of how quantities are related. You can use a graph to estimate a solution. You can also formally solve equations to determine exact values.

Practice

A shuttle space suit, including the life support system, weighs about 310 pounds. The break in the y-axis represents the values from 0–300.

1. What does each ordered pair on the line represent?
2. Write an equation to represent the relationship shown in the graph.
3. Is this a proportional relationship? Justify your answer.
4. In this problem situation, do all the points on the line make sense? Explain your reasoning.
5. Determine the weight of an astronaut without the shuttle suit given that the astronaut's weight while wearing the shuttle suit.
   a. 480 lb
   b. 467 lb
   c. 520 lb

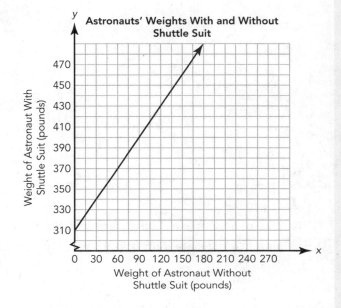

The gravitational pull of the Moon is not as great as that on Earth. In fact, if a person checks their weight on the Moon, it will be only $\frac{1}{6}$ of their weight on Earth.

6. What does each ordered pair on the line represent?
7. Write an equation to represent the relationship shown in the graph.
8. Is this a proportional relationship? Justify your answer.
9. In this problem situation, do all the points on the graph make sense?
10. Determine the weight of a person on Earth given his weight on the Moon.
    a. 12 lb
    b. 21 lb
    c. 36 lb

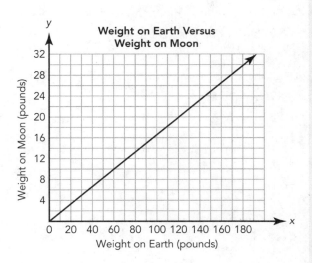

Stretch

Write an equation to represent each of the three segments of the graph shown. List any restrictions in the possible x-values.

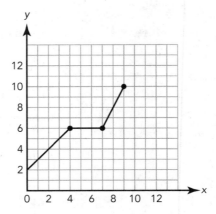

Review

Solve for each unknown value.

1. The area of a triangle is 12.5 square feet and the height is 6 feet. Determine the base of the triangle.
2. The area of a parallelogram is 74.8 square feet and the base is 22 feet. Determine the height of the parallelogram.

Determine the independent and dependent quantities in each scenario.

3. Selena is driving to her grandmother's house. She travels an average of 60 miles per hour.
4. On her way to work each morning, Sophia purchases a cup of coffee for each of her colleagues and pays $2.25 per cup the coffee shop.

Use long division to determine each quotient.

5. 1968 ÷ 12
6. 2363 ÷ 139

Planes, Trains, and Paychecks

Multiple Representations of Equations

WARM UP

Identify two quantities in each situation. Then state which quantity depends on the other.

1. Snow is falling at a rate of 3 inches per hour.

2. The outside temperature is increasing at an average of 10 degrees each day.

3. The car wash generated an average profit of $8.00 per car.

4. The income from the sale of movie tickets was $8.50 per person.

5. A dog groomer charges $35 for every dog.

LEARNING GOALS

- Write and solve equations that represent relationships given in tables, graphs, and situations.
- Identify independent and dependent quantities represented in tables, graphs, and scenarios.
- Analyze the relationship between the independent and dependent quantities in a situation using graphs, tables, and equations.
- Determine whether the data represented in a graph of an equation are discrete or continuous.

You have identified independent and dependent quantities in relationships and have expressed these relationships using equations. How can you relate independent and dependent quantities in a variety of different situations, using a variety of different representations?

To the Equation-Mobile!

A mobile (MO-beel) is hanging art. It features all kinds of different objects suspended from string or wire. Balance is important to the visual effect of mobiles.

Determine what value each shape represents in each mobile.

1.

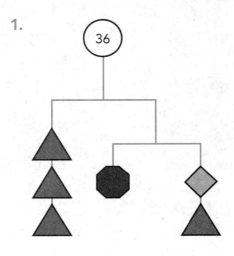

2.

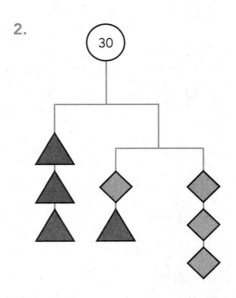

SnapSmart charges the same price for each 3 in. by 4 in. picture print.

1. The table shows a few orders and the cost of each.

    a. What is the cost of one print? Explain how you determined the cost.

    b. Define variables for the quantities in this situation. Then write an equation that models the relationship between these quantities.

Number of Prints	Cost ($)
10	1.20
32	3.84
50	6.00
110	13.20

    c. Create a graph for this situation.

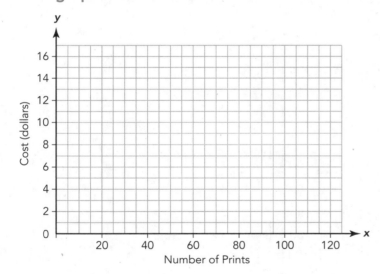

    d. Tell whether the quantities in the SnapSmart scenario are discrete or continuous. Explain your reasoning.

    e. You can draw a line to show the shape of the graph. Do all the points on the line make sense in this scenario?

2. The table shows the cost of a particular item.

Number of Items	Cost ($)
1	6
8	48
16	96
5	30

a. Describe how the cost is related to the number of items.

b. Define variables for the quantities in this situation. Then write an equation that models the relationship between these quantities.

c. Explain whether the quantities in this situation are discrete or continuous.

d. Create a graph for this situation.

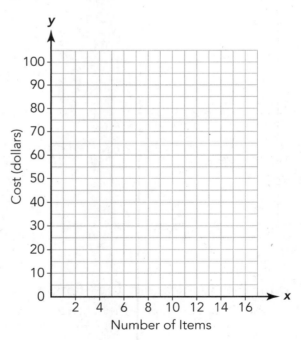

e. What do you notice about the shape of the graph? You can connect the points to see the shape.

3. Read each situation and analyze the corresponding table of values. Identify the independent and dependent quantities in each. Then, write an equation that models the relationship between the quantities.

   a. The total profit made on cutting lawns and the profit made by each person are represented in the table shown.

Total Profit Made ($)	Profit Made by Each Person ($)
21	7.00
25.50	8.50
45	15.00

   b. The number of boxes of cookies sold and the total profit are represented in the table shown.

Boxes of Cookies Sold	Total Profit ($)
3	7.50
5	12.50
7	17.50

   A table of values can be represented vertically or horizontally.

   c. The number of tiles required to complete a job and the number of tiles ordered are represented in the table shown.

Number of Tiles Required	75	95	115
Number of Tiles Ordered	90	110	130

ACTIVITY 3.2 Equations from Graphs

The graph shows the relationship between the distance of a train from the station and the time in minutes.

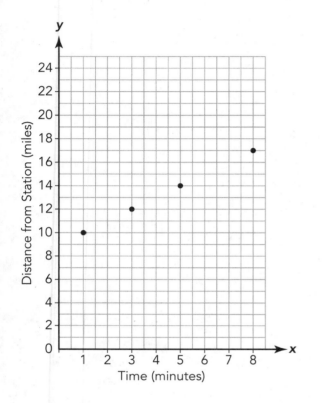

1. Complete the table using the points from the graph.

2. Define variables and write an equation to represent the relationship between the quantities.

3. How far is the train from the station after 20 minutes?

4. Connect the points to show the shape of the graph. Do all of the values on the line make sense in this situation?

The graph shows the relationship between the height of a plane and its distance from the airport in miles.

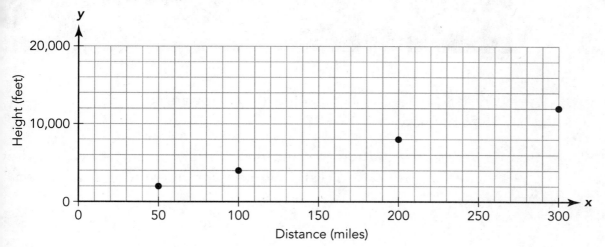

Distance (miles)

5. Complete the table using the points from the graph.

6. Write an equation to represent the relationship between the quantities.

7. What is the height of the plane at 150 miles?

8. Connect the points to show the shape of the graph. Do all of the values on the line make sense in this situation?

ACTIVITY 3.3   Equations from Scenarios

Crystal got a job working at the local hardware store making $8.76 per hour.

1. Write an equation that models the relationship between the number of hours Crystal worked and how much she earned.

2. How much would Crystal earn if she worked the given times.

   a. 5 hours

   b. $2\frac{1}{2}$ hours

   c. 5 hours and 30 minutes

   d. 10 hours and 15 minutes

3. Use your equation to calculate the number of hours Crystal worked given her total pay.

   a. $218.75

   b. $293.46

   c. $203.67

4. Complete the table.

Time Worked (hours)	Earnings ($)
5	
2.5	
5.5	
10.25	
	218.75
	293.46
	203.67

5. Use the table to complete the graph.

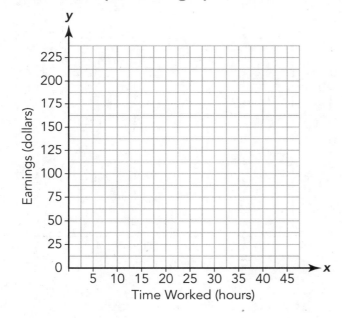

6. Connect the points to show the shape of the graph. Do all of the points on the line make sense in this situation?

7. Jake's dog eats an average of 40 pounds of dry dog food in one month.

   a. Write an equation to model the relationship between the number of pounds of dog food and the number of months.

   b. Complete the table and graph.

Time (months)	Amount of Dog Food (lb)
0	
1	
2	
	120
	160
	200

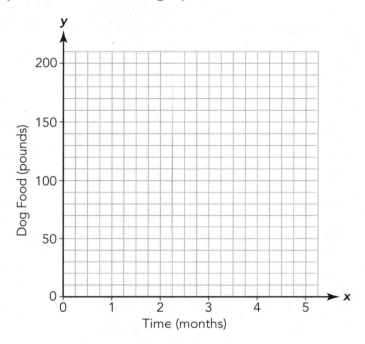

   c. Connect the points to show the shape of the graph. Do all of the points on the line make sense in this situation?

TALK the TALK 💬

Let Us Organize the Ways

Multiple representations—including drawings or diagrams, verbal descriptions, tables, graphs, and equations—can be useful in analyzing and solving problems.

1. Complete the graphic organizer by describing the advantages of each representation.

   - verbal
   - table
   - graph
   - equation

VERBAL

TABLE

MULTIPLE
REPRESENTATIONS

GRAPH

EQUATION

Assignment

Write

Create an algebraic equation. Represent the equation using a word problem, a table, and a graph.

Remember

When a quantity can have values that are only counting numbers, it is called a discrete quantity. When a quantity can have any value, it is called a continuous quantity.

Practice

1. Lashawna works at the local candy shop. The bulk candy is sold by the pound. Customers place the candy they would like to buy in a plastic bucket, and then Lashawna weighs it to determine how much the customer owes. Before calculating the price, Lashawna must subtract the weight of the plastic bucket. The candy bucket weighs 0.72 pound.

   a. Complete the table.

   b. Write an equation that models the relationship between the quantities in this situation.

   c. Use the table to create a graph of the relationship.

   d. Explain whether all points on the line make sense.

Total Weight (lb)	Weight of Candy (lb)
2.84	
3.00	
	0.71
0.98	
	1.71
	1.13

2. Lashawna is packaging some bulk candy for a sale. The price is $3.98 per pound.

   a. Write an equation to model the relationship between the total cost and the weight of the candy.

   b. Complete the table.

   c. Use the table to create a graph of the relationship.

   d. Explain whether it makes sense to connect the points on your graph.

Total Cost ($)	Weight of Candy (lb)
	2.50
	3.20
4.98	
	1.97
9.47	
13.93	

Stretch

A cryptarithm is a puzzle which replaces digits with letters. Your job is to use reasoning to determine what digits the letters stand for. When two letters are the same, they represent the same digit. When the letters are different, they represent different digits.

In this famous cryptarithm, the sum is correct. Can you solve it?

```
    S  E  N  D
+   M  O  R  E
————————————————
 M  O  N  E  Y
```

Review

Use the graph to estimate each solution.

1. How long did it take Serena to travel 70 miles?

2. How long did it take to burn 100 calories?

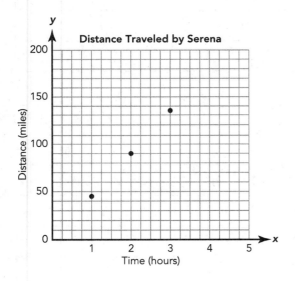

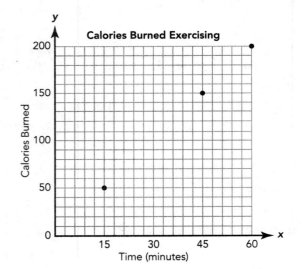

Write each statement as an algebraic expression.

3. five less than twice a number

4. seven and one half more than a number

Solve each equation.

5. $20 = 6x$

6. $15.5 + p = 44$

Triathlon Training

Relating Distance, Rate, and Time

WARM UP

1. Express 3 hours and 15 minutes as a decimal.

2. Express 3 hours and 15 minutes in terms of minutes.

3. Express 2.75 hours in terms of hours and minutes.

4. Express 2.75 hours in terms of minutes.

LEARNING GOALS

- Use multiple representations to solve one-step real-world and mathematical problems.
- Analyze the relationship between independent and dependent quantities using graphs, tables, and equations.
- Summarize the relationship between distance, rate, and time.

You have graphed and analyzed a variety of relationships between two quantities. Some quantities are often grouped together. One set of such quantities is distance, rate, and time. What relationship exists between these quantities?

Gearing Up for the Olympics

Deazia has her sights set on competing in the triathlon in the 2024 Summer Olympics. A triathlon includes three sports: swimming, cycling, and running. Deazia must build up her endurance to be able complete all three events in quick succession!

As part of her training, Deazia will participate in a variety of triathlons over the next year. The table provides the distances for each leg of five different triathlons.

	Island Escape	Kid Zone	Olympic Style	Sprint	SuperTri
Swim	1.5 mi	600 m	1.5 km	750 m	2.4 mi
Cycle	18 mi	15 km	40 km	20 km	112 mi
Run	8 mi	5 km	10 km	5 km	26.2 mi

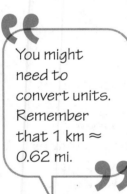

You might need to convert units. Remember that 1 km ≈ 0.62 mi.

1. **What is the total distance covered in each triathlon?**

2. **If Deazia completes all 5 triathlons in one year, how many miles will she swim during these competitions? How many miles will she cycle? How many miles will she run?**

Swimming is the first leg of the triathlon, so Deazia has trained with a coach to improve her chance of getting off to a great start.

Deazia's coach plotted her times and distances from her last few training sessions. Based on the data, the coach drew in a line to represent an approximation of her average speed.

Deazia's swimming speed is a unit rate.

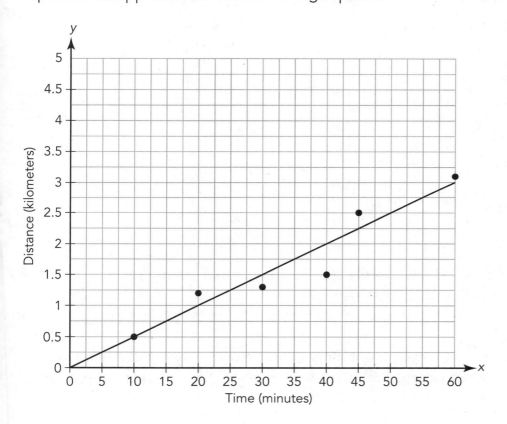

1. Deazia's little sister thinks that all of Deazia's (time, distance) points should be on the line drawn by her coach. Is she correct? Explain your reasoning.

2. Use the graph to determine Deazia's average swimming rate.

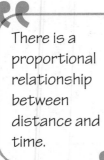

There is a proportional relationship between distance and time.

Deazia wants to know how long it will take her to complete the swimming segment of each triathlon. She decides to start with the Olympic Style triathlon, which has a 1.5 km swim leg.

WORKED EXAMPLE

$$\frac{\text{distance}}{\text{time}} = \frac{1 \text{ km}}{20 \text{ minutes}}$$

$$\frac{1.5 \text{ km}}{\text{time}} = \frac{1 \text{ km}}{20 \text{ minutes}}$$

$\times 1.5$

$$\frac{1.5 \text{ km}}{\text{time}} = \frac{1 \text{ km}}{20 \text{ minutes}}$$

$\times 1.5$

It should take Deazia 30 minutes to complete the swim segment of the Olympic Style triathlon.

---

3. Assuming Deazia swims at her average rate, determine how long it should take her to complete the swimming segment of the four remaining triathlons.

    a. Island Escape   **b.** Kid Zone

    c. Sprint   **d.** SuperTri

4. Write an equation to represent the amount of time, t, required for Deazia to swim a given distance, d.

5. Write another equation to represent the distance, d, Deazia can swim for a given amount of time, t.

6. Deazia's coach surprised her with an entry into a secret triathlon, the Mystic, last weekend.

   a. If she swam at her average rate and completed the swim segment in 45 minutes, how long was the swim segment? Explain your reasoning.

   b. How could you use a different strategy to verify your answer?

ACTIVITY 4.2 Cycling Rate

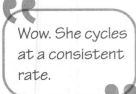

Wow. She cycles at a consistent rate.

Deazia cycles as a regular part of her training schedule. After each ride, she records her distances and times in a table.

Distance Biked (kilometers)	Time (hours)
5	$\frac{1}{4}$
35	$1\frac{3}{4}$
90	$4\frac{1}{2}$

1. Determine Deazia's cycling rate in minutes per kilometer and in kilometers per minute.

2. Deazia would like to predict how long it will take her to complete the cycling segment of each triathlon. She thinks she should use the *minutes per kilometer* rate but her sister says that she should use the *kilometers per minute* rate. Who's correct? Explain your reasoning.

3. Assuming she cycles at the same average rate, how long should it take Deazia to complete the cycling segment of each triathlon?

    a. Island Escape

    b. Kid Zone

    c. Olympic Style

    d. Sprint

    e. SuperTri

In this scenario, time is the dependent variable.

4. Write an equation to determine the amount of time required for Deazia to cycle a given distance.

5. Use your results to create a graph of the time, in minutes, that Deazia cycles versus the distance she cycles, in kilometers. Connect the plotted points.

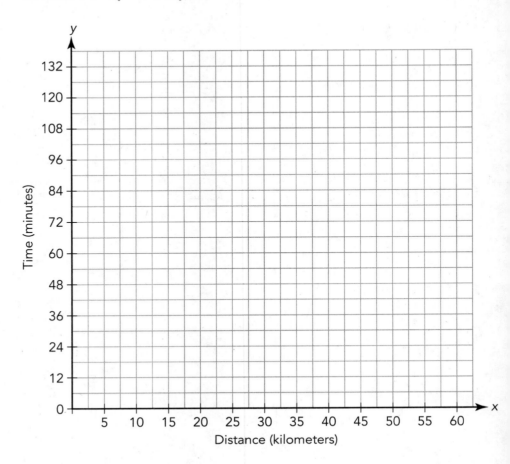

6. You cannot graph the time and distance for the SuperTri on this graph. Explain how you know it would be on the line if the graph were extended.

7. In the Mystic triathlon, the cycling segment is 35 kilometers. Use your graph to estimate how long it should take Deazia to complete this segment of the triathlon. Explain your strategy.

Deazia runs every day as part of her training routine. She averages 9 minutes per mile.

1. Write an equation to determine the amount of time required to run a given distance.

2. Use your equation to determine how long will it take Deazia to complete the running segment of each triathlon.

   a. Island Escape   b. Kid Zone

   c. Olympic Style   d. Sprint

   e. SuperTri

3. Use your equation and the results from Question 2 to create a graph of time, in minutes, that Deazia runs versus her distance, in miles. Connect the plotted points.

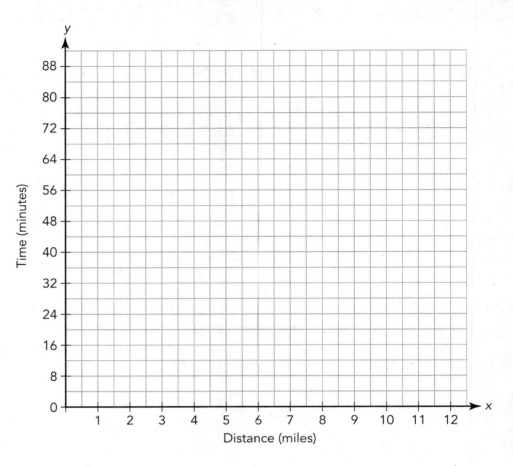

Assume that Deazia runs at her average rate in this triathlon.

4. After competing in the Mystic triathlon, Deazia reports that it took her 87 minutes to complete the running segment. Use the graph to estimate the length of the running segment of this triathlon.

5. Rewrite the equation in Question 1 in order to determine the distance traveled for a given amount of time.

6. Use your new equation to determine the actual length of the running segment of the Mystic.

TALK the TALK

Reflecting on Triathlon Training

To analyze the three segments of the triathlons, you used distances traveled, times traveled, and rates.

1. Record the two equations that could be used to describe each leg of the race.

- determine the distance, given the time

- determine the time, given the distance

	Determine Distance	Determine Time
Swim		
Cycle		
Run		

2. What do you notice about the coefficients in the equations? Why does this make sense?

3. Write the ratio, including units, represented in the *Determine Distance* equation for each segment of the race.

4. Explain why the ratios, or rates, listed in Question 3, not their reciprocals, are the appropriate rates to use in determining distance.

Assignment

Write

Suppose your work partner was absent today. Write at least three sentences that summarize the relationship between *distance* (*d*), *rate* (*r*), and *time* (*t*). Be sure to talk about some of the multiple representations (verbal statements, graphs, tables, equations) of the relationship.

Remember

The equation that relates distance, rate, and time is often written as $d = rt$.

Practice

1. An airplane takes off and climbs at a constant rate of 1400 feet per minute.
   a. Write an equation to model the relationship between the plane's altitude and the time in minutes.
   b. Complete the table.

Time (min)	Altitude (ft)
1	
1.5	
2	
2.5	

   c. Use the equation to determine how much time it takes for the plane to reach an altitude of 3 miles.
2. A helium balloon rises at a constant rate of 200 feet per minute.
   a. Write an equation to model the relationship between the balloon's altitude and the time in minutes.
   b. Graph the equation.
   c. Use your graph to determine how much time it takes for the balloon to reach an altitude of 700 feet.
3. A car travels on the interstate at a constant speed. The distances are recorded in a table.

Distance (miles)	Time (hours)
16.25	0.25
32.5	0.5
260	4
390	6

   a. Determine the car's rate in miles per hour and in hours per mile.
   b. Write an equation to determine the amount of time required to travel a given distance.
   c. Use the table to create a graph of the time versus the distance traveled.
   d. Determine how many minutes it will take the car to travel 43 miles.

Stretch

Alison and her friend are traveling home from New Jersey on Route 28. Alison thinks that taking Route 66 to Route 80 is a faster way home. Alison's friend says that staying on Route 28 is shorter, so they will make it home faster. Who's correct? Which path is faster? By how much?

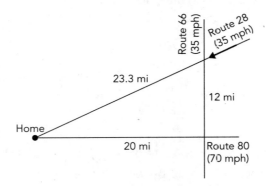

Review

1. A business subtracts $7.50 from each employees' gross weekly pay to cover the cost of their uniforms.
   a. Define variables for an employee's gross weekly pay and for an employee's weekly pay after the uniform fee.
   b. Write an equation that models the relationship between the variables.
   c. Graph the equation. Is the graph discrete or continuous?
   d. Calculate the gross weekly pay if the pay after the uniform fee was $67.23.

2. Determine each answer using the given formula.
   a. The formula $P = 4s$ is used to calculate the perimeter, P, of a square with a side length, s. Calculate the length of a side of the square if its perimeter is 34.56 inches.
   b. The formula $P = a + b + c$ is used to calculate the perimeter, P, of a triangle with side lengths a, b, and c. Calculate the unknown side length for a triangle with a perimeter of 52.81 inches and two sides measuring 16.32 inches each.

3. Calculate the area of each triangle.
   a.
   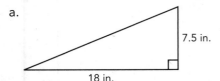
   7.5 in.
   18 in.

   b.
   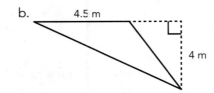
   4.5 m
   4 m

Graphing Quantitative Relationships Summary

KEY TERMS

- discrete graph
- continuous graph
- dependent quantity
- independent quantity
- independent variable
- dependent variable

LESSON 1 — Every Graph Tells a Story

A **discrete graph** is a graph of isolated points. Often, those points are counting numbers.

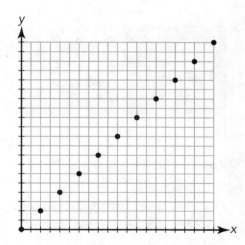

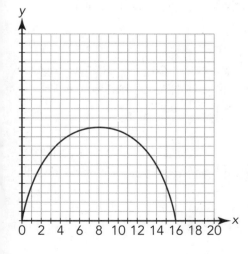

A **continuous graph** is a graph with no breaks in it. Each point on a continuous graph, even those represented by fractional numbers, represents a solution to the graphed scenario.

When one quantity depends on another in a real-world problem situation, it is said to be the **dependent quantity**. The quantity on which it depends is called the **independent quantity**. The variable that represents the independent quantity is called the **independent variable**, and the variable that represents the dependent quantity is called the **dependent variable**.

For example, suppose you are draining a 150-gallon fish tank at a rate of 15 gallons per minute. How much water remains in the tank at a specific time?

In this scenario, the independent quantity is time, measured in minutes, and the dependent quantity is the number of gallons of water in the fish tank. The equation that represents the scenario is $w = 125 - 15t$. The independent variable is t, which represents the number of minutes, and the dependent variable is w, which represents the gallons of water in the tank.

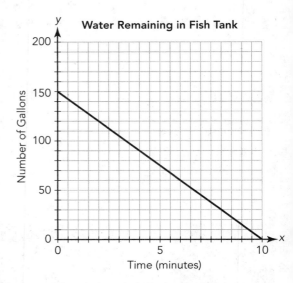

Note that the independent quantity is plotted on the horizontal axis and the dependent quantity is plotted on the vertical axis.

LESSON
2

The Power of the Horizontal Line

You can use a graph to determine an independent quantity given a dependent quantity.

For example, Nic sells pretzels for $1.25 each morning at the games held at the Community Center. The amount of money collected for the number of pretzels sold can be represented by points on the graph. The equation corresponding to the graph is $y = 1.25x$. You can use the graph to determine how many pretzels Nic sold if he collected $10.

First, locate 10 on the y-axis and draw a horizontal line. This shows that $10 is the amount of money collected. The x-value of the point where your horizontal line intersects with the graph of 1.25x is the number of pretzels sold for $10.

If you are given a graph, a solution to the equation represented by the graphed line is any point on that line. Nic sold 8 pretzels if he collected $10.

In some problem situations, when you model a relationship with a line, not all the points on the line will make sense. It is up to you to interpret the meaning of data values from the line drawn on a graph for each situation.

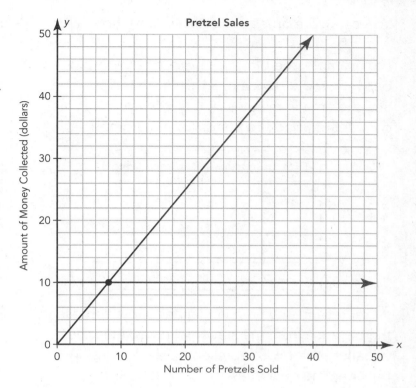

Pretzel Sales

Planes, Trains, and Paychecks

You can write an equation from a relationship given in a table.

For example, the number of tiles required to complete a job and the number of tiles ordered are represented in the table shown.

Number of Tiles Required	60	75	100
Number of Tiles Ordered	80	95	120

The independent quantity is the number of tiles required to complete a job and the dependent quantity is the number of tiles ordered. By analyzing the table, you can see that the number of tiles ordered is always 20 more than the number of tiles required. An equation that models this relationship is $y = x + 20$.

You can write an equation from a relationship represented in a graph.

For example, the graph shows the relationship between the distance of a train from the station and the time in minutes. A table of values can be completed using the points from the graph.

Time (minutes)	Distance (miles)
1	9
2	10
4	12
7	15

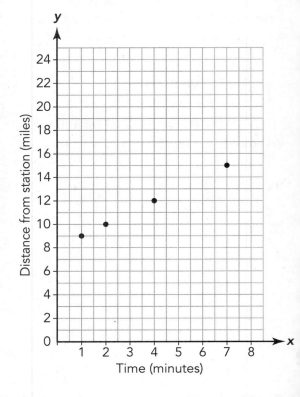

If t represents the time in minutes and d represents the distance from the station in miles, then the equation $d = t + 8$ represents the relationship between the quantities.

You can write an equation from a scenario.

For example, Deanna got a job working at the post office making $10.25 per hour.

An equation that models the relationship between the number of hours Deanna worked and the amount of money she earned can be written. Let a represent the amount Deanna earned and h represent the number of hours she worked. The equation is $a = 10.25h$.

The equation that relates distance, rate, and time is often written as $d = rt$.

For example, Deazia is training for a triathlon. Deazia's coach plotted her times and distances from her last few swimming training sessions. Based on the data, the coach drew in a line to represent an approximation of her average speed.

Deazia's swimming speed is a unit rate. There is a proportional relationship between distance and time.

Deazia wants to know how long it will take her to swim 1.5 km.

$$\frac{\text{distance}}{\text{time}} = \frac{1 \text{ km}}{20 \text{ minutes}}$$

$$\frac{1.5 \text{ km}}{\text{time}} = \frac{1 \text{ km}}{20 \text{ minutes}}$$

$\times 1.5$

$$\frac{1.5 \text{ km}}{\text{time}} = \frac{1 \text{ km}}{20 \text{ minutes}}$$

$\times 1.5$

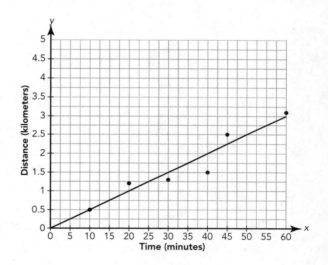

It should take Deazia 30 minutes to complete the swimming segment of the Olympic Style triathlon.

MODULE 4

MOVING BEYOND POSITIVE QUANTITIES

The lessons in this module extend your understanding of numbers and the number line to include negative numbers. You will use a number line to represent, make sense of, and order negative numbers. You will build on your knowledge of the coordinate plane to construct a four-quadrant graph. Throughout the module, you will analyze and solve a variety of real-world problems.

TOPIC 1
Signed Numbers

If you think of the surface of the ocean as 0, then a diver is in the negative numbers until he comes back up.

Module 4: Moving Beyond Positive Quantities

TOPIC 1: SIGNED NUMBERS

In this topic, students are formally introduced to negative numbers. Students begin by reflecting the positive numbers across zero to build the rational number line. They focus on the meaning assigned to positive and negative rational numbers, with particular focus on the meaning of 0 in real-world and mathematical situations. Students develop an understanding of the relationship between opposites and distance on a number line, leading to the concept of absolute value. Throughout this topic, students continue to develop their fluency with whole numbers, fractions, and decimals.

Where have we been?

Prior to grade 6, students positioned whole numbers, fractions, and decimals on number lines and operated with these numbers using number lines as references. The opening activities in this topic draw on this prior knowledge of number lines and numbers' positions relative to each other. In previous lessons in this course, students learned about and ordered non-negative rational numbers.

Where are we going?

Students will operate on signed numbers beginning in grade 7. The foundation provided in this topic will enable students to develop strategies for operating with signed numbers. Students will continue using the ideas from this topic throughout the remainder of the course. Just as they reflected the number line to include negative values, in the next topic students will reflect the first quadrant of a coordinate plane to create the four-quadrant coordinate plane.

Using a Number Line to Visualize Opposites

Each positive integer has an opposite, negative integer, and vice versa. The negative sign reflects a number across 0 on the number line. For example, the opposite of 3 is −3. Furthermore, the opposite of an opposite is the original number, e.g., −(−3) = 3.

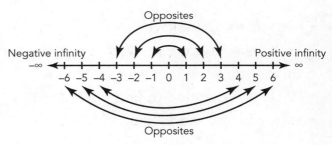

Myth: Cramming for a test is just as good as spaced practice for long-term retention.

Everyone has been there. You have a big test tomorrow, but you've been so busy that you haven't had time to study. So you had to learn it all in one night. You may have received a decent grade on the test. However, did you remember the material a week, month, or a year later?

The honest answer is, "probably not." That's because long-term memory is designed to retain useful information. How does your brain know if a memory is "useful" or not? One way is the frequency in which you encounter a piece of information. If you see something only once (like during cramming), then your brain doesn't deem those memories as important. However, if you sporadically come across the same information over time, then it's probably important. To optimize retention, encourage your student to periodically study the same information over expanding intervals of time.

#mathmythbusted

Talking Points

You can further support your student's learning by resisting the urge, as long as possible, to get to the answer in a problem that your student is working on. Students are encountering negative numbers formally for the first time in this topic. They will need time and space to struggle with all the implications of working with this expanded number system. Practice asking good questions when your student is stuck.

Questions to Ask

- Let's think about this. What are all the things you know?
- What do you need to find out?
- How can you model this problem?

Key Terms

opposites
Opposite numbers are reflections of each other across 0 on the number line.

negative numbers
The values to the left of zero on the number line are called negative numbers and are labeled with a negative sign.

absolute value
The absolute value of a number is its distance from zero on a number line.

Human Number Line

Introduction to Negative Numbers

1

WARM UP

Plot each number on a number line. Then, insert a > or < symbol to make each inequality statement true.

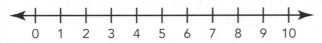

1. $\frac{3}{4}$ _____ $1\frac{1}{2}$

2. 5.6 _____ 5.06

3. 7.65 _____ 6.75

LEARNING GOALS

- Use positive and negative numbers to describe quantities having opposite directions.
- Explain the meaning of 0 in contexts represented by positive and negative numbers.
- Identify and represent a number and its opposite on a number line.
- Represent, interpret, and order positive and negative integers and other rational numbers using number lines and inequality statements.

KEY TERMS

- negative numbers
- infinity

You have used numbers equal to or greater than 0 to represent real-world situations. But how can you use numbers less than 0 to describe real-world situations?

Number Line Geography

1. What do you know about a number line?

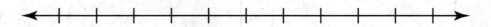

2. Label the number line and be sure to include 0. Then plot and label a single point of your choice on the number line.

   a. Draw a ray, or an arrow, beginning at your point to represent the numbers larger than the value at your point.

   b. Draw a ray, or an arrow, beginning at your point to represent the numbers smaller than the value at your point.

   c. At the ends of a number line, there are arrows going in both directions. What do these arrows indicate?

   d. What do you think is on the number line to the left of 0?

Investigating Time on a Number Line

Let's use a number line to represent time.

Your teacher will assign students to participate in the activity.
Be sure to record what happens on the number line.

1. For each student, plot and label the point where the student stands on the number line. Also identify what time is represented by the point.

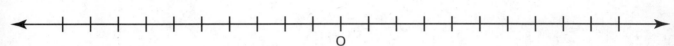

0

Student A: Stand at 0 to represent the time right now.
Student B: Stand at the point that represents 3 hours from now.
Student C: Stand at the point that represents 3 hours ago.
Student D: Stand at the point that represents 5 hours from now.
Student E: Stand at the point that represents 2 hours ago.
Student F: Stand at the point that represents 7 hours ago.

A number line can be created by reflecting the positive numbers across zero. The values to the left of zero on the number line are called **negative numbers** and are labeled with a negative sign. The positive values extend to positive infinity, and the negative numbers extend to negative infinity. **Infinity**, represented by the symbol ∞, means a quantity with no end or bound. The number line goes on forever in both directions!

A negative number is written with a negative sign. You can write a positive number with a positive sign or without any sign. For example, positive 5 can be written as +5 or 5.

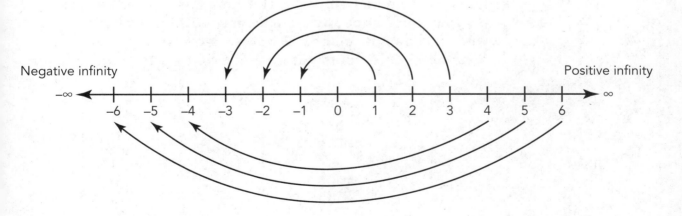

Negative infinity

Positive infinity

2. Describe the change in the values of the numbers as you move to the right on the number line.

3. Describe the change in the values of the numbers as you move to the left on the number line.

Consider your class time number line.

4. Describe the locations of the points that represent time in the future.

5. Describe the locations of the points that represent time in the past.

6. How would your number line be labeled differently from one created by a class that starts at a different time?

7. What observations can you make about where a given number of hours before or after time 0 is plotted? What do you notice about its distance from 0? For example, what do you notice about 3 hours before and 3 hours after now? Or 6 hours before and 6 hours after now?

Representing Opposites on a Number Line

Let's think more about both sides of 0 on a number line.

Your teacher will model a number line.

1. Create and label a number line according to the model.

2. Plot and label the location where each student stands on the number line. In the table, identify the value represented by the location where the student is standing.

   Student A: Stand at 0.
   Student B: Stand at 4.5.
   Student C: Stand at the opposite of 4.5.
   Student D: Stand at −6.
   Student E: Stand at the opposite of −6.
   Student F: Stand at a location between 2 and 3.
   Student G: Stand at the location that is the opposite of
                  Student F.

Student	Value
A	
B	
C	
D	
E	
F	
G	

3. Describe the number line relationship of the students who were opposites of each other.

There is only one number that is its own opposite.

Opposite numbers are reflections of each other across 0 on the number line.

- The opposite of a positive number is a corresponding negative number.

- The opposite of a negative number is a corresponding positive number.

Attaching a negative sign to a number means reflecting that number across 0 on the number line.

4. **Use symbols to represent the opposite of 4.5 and the value it represents.**

   $-(4.5) = $ _____

5. **Use symbols to represent the opposite of −6 and the value it represents.**

   $-(-6) = $ _____

6. **What do you notice about the distance from 0 of corresponding opposite numbers?**

Don't forget to label the number line!

7. **What is the opposite of 0?**

8. **Name the opposite of each number. Then, plot each number and its opposite on the number line.**

   a. $1\frac{1}{2}$ b. −5   c. −9.9

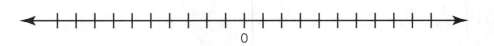

0

Representing Money on a Number Line

Alyson and her friends are trying to decide if they can go to the movies. Each ticket costs $9.00. After checking their wallets, each friend comments on how much money they have.

- Alyson: I have $2.50 more than the movie costs.

- Sharon: Oh, I don't have enough money. I'm $4.00 short.

- Brian: Not only can I buy a ticket, but I have just enough money to buy the $8.00 snack combo!

- Eileen: If I can find one more quarter, I can go.

Myron and Paulie created different number lines to represent the scenario.

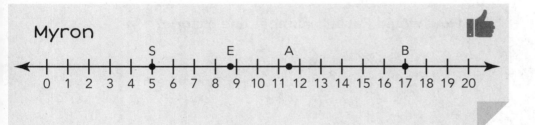

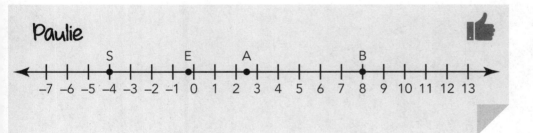

Analyze each representation of the scenario.

1. **What does each point represent on Myron's number line?**

2. **What does each point represent on Paulie's number line?**

3. Myron and Paulie are thinking about 0 differently. Explain what 0 represents on each number line.

A matinee is a movie played at a theater in the afternoon.

4. Suppose the four friends decide to go to a matinee instead, where the ticket price is $7.50.

   a. How would Myron's number line change?

   b. How would Paulie's number line change?

Temperature Connection

Number lines can also be vertical, like a thermometer or a measure of elevation.

1. Discuss and write a sentence to describe the meaning of each statement.

   a. The weather forecaster predicts the temperature will be below zero.

   b. A submarine travels at 3000 feet below sea level.

   c. Badwater Basin in Death Valley, California, is 86 meters below sea level.

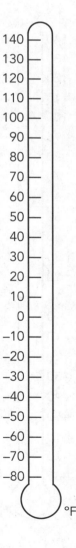

2. Mark each temperature on the thermometer shown.

   a. The highest temperature on record in the United States is 134°F. It occurred in 1913 in Death Valley, California.

   b. The lowest temperature on record is −80°F. It occurred at Prospect Creek Camp, Alaska.

   c. The lowest temperature recorded in the contiguous 48 states is −70°F. It occurred in Montana.

   d. The highest winter average temperature in the United States is 78°F, which occurs in Honolulu, Hawaii.

3. Which is colder, the lowest temperature recorded in Alaska or the lowest temperature recorded in Montana? How do you know?

4. Yadi and Eric were comparing 25 degrees to −27 degrees.

   • Yadi wrote 25 < −27 and justified her comparison by stating that the further a number is from zero, the greater the number.

   • Eric wrote 25 > −27 and justified his comparison by stating that the greater temperature will be above the second temperature on a thermometer.

   Who is correct? Explain your choice.

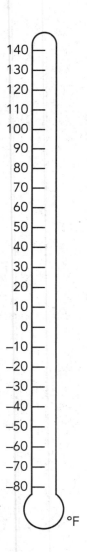

5. Plot each set of temperatures on the thermometer. Then insert a > or < symbol to make each number sentence true.

   a. −26°F _____ −31°F

   b. −6°F _____ −17°F

   c. −9°F _____ 8°F

6. Order the temperatures from least to greatest.

   25°F   −33°F   0°F   105°F   −40°F   −5°F   67°F

Comparing and Ordering Rational Numbers

Helen and Grace started a company called Top Notch. They check the company's bank balance at the end of each week. The table shown represents the first 10 weeks of operation. Overdrafts, or weeks when they owe the bank money, are represented by amounts within parentheses. For example, ($25) denotes an overdraft of $25; they owe the bank $25. Amounts that are not in parentheses are when they made money.

Week	1	2	3	4	5	6	7	8	9	10
Balance	$159	($201)	$231	($456)	($156)	($12)	$281	$175	$192	$213
+/− Number										

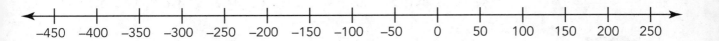

1. Use the table and number line to answer each question.

   a. Write each as a positive or negative number and then plot the number on the number line.

   b. What does 0 represent in this situation?

   c. In which week did they have the highest bank balance?

   d. In which week did they show greatest overdraft?

2. For each pair of weeks, write an inequality statement to compare the positive and negative numbers. Interpret the statement in context.

   a. Week 1 and Week 5   b. Week 4 and Week 6

You can compare different types of numbers by plotting the numbers on a number line.

3. Use the number line to answer each question.

   a. Plot each value on the number line.

   $$-6\frac{2}{3} \quad -20 \quad 0 \quad 10.5 \quad -17\frac{1}{2} \quad -7.98 \quad 12 \quad -3 \quad -13$$

   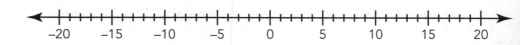

   b. Which of the numbers has the least value? How do you know?

   c. Which of the numbers has the greatest value? How do you know?

   d. Order the numbers from least to greatest.

4. Plot each rational number on the number line. Then, insert a >, <, or = symbol to make each number sentence true.

   a. -10.25 _____ $-15\frac{2}{3}$

   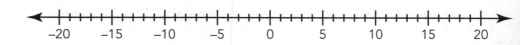

   b. -17 _____ -17

   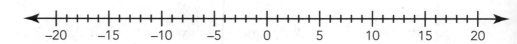

   c. $5\frac{2}{3}$ _____ -8.28

   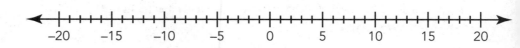

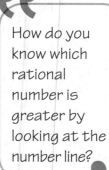

How do you know which rational number is greater by looking at the number line?

TALK the TALK 💬

Putting It All Together

1. What does 0 mean on a number line?

2. What does *opposite* mean in terms of a number line?

3. Compare the types of numbers. Use what you know about number lines to explain your reasoning.

   a. Which is greater—a negative or a positive rational number?

   b. Which is greater—zero or any positive rational number?

   c. Which is greater—zero or any negative rational number?

   d. How do you decide which of two numbers is greater if both numbers are positive?

   e. How do you decide which of two numbers is greater if both numbers are negative?

4. Your sixth grade cousin goes to school in a different state. His math class has not yet started comparing integers. Write him an email explaining how to compare any two numbers. Be sure to include 1 or 2 examples and enough details that he will be able to explain it to his class.

_____

_____

_____

_____

_____

_____

_____

_____

_____

_____

_____

_____

Assignment

Write

Write a sentence to explain the relationship between *opposites* and *negative numbers*.

Remember

The rational number line is used to represent positive numbers, negative numbers, and zero. The values to the left of zero on the number line are reflections of the values on the right across 0.

Practice

1. Plot each number and its opposite on the number line.
   a. -1
   b. 0.1
   c. $1\frac{3}{4}$
   d. -1.9
   e. 0.009

2. Order the numbers from least to greatest.

   $0.125 \quad 1\frac{1}{5} \quad -\frac{4}{9} \quad \frac{4}{11} \quad -\frac{3}{2} \quad -2.75$

3. The Ravine Flyer II is a steel and wood roller coaster that takes advantage of the terrain in Erie, PA, to make the ride more exciting. Although the coaster is only 80 feet high, it follows the line of a cliff in order to drop to -35 feet (0 represents the height of the cliff).
   a. Plot the highest and lowest points of the roller coaster on a vertical number line.
   b. Explain why a vertical number line better represents the problem context than a horizontal number line.
   c. How many total feet does the roller coaster drop?

4. The Monster is a roller coaster that uses a design similar to the Ravine Flyer II. The Monster reaches a height of 120 feet, but then drops to -25 feet. Order the highest and lowest points of the two roller coasters from least to greatest.

5. An amusement park wants to design a coaster that rises 60 feet above ground and then drops the same distance below ground through a tunnel. Represent the underground depth with a number, and explain its relationship with the above ground height.

Stretch

Create a new situation, similar to Activity 1.3 *Representing Money on a Number Line*, in which zero can have two different meanings.

Review

Name the two quantities that are changing in each and determine which quantity is the dependent quantity and which is the independent quantity.

1. Terrence types 80 words per minute.

2. To determine the total weekly wages of his employees, Mr. Jackson multiplies the total number of hours his employees work by $12.

3. A mountain climber is ascending a mountain at a rate of 5 feet per minute. Define variables and write an equation that represents the situation. Graph the equation on a coordinate plane.

Perform the indicated operation.

4. $11\frac{4}{5} + 5\frac{2}{3}$

5. $\frac{27}{4} \div \frac{3}{2}$

Magnificent Magnitude

2

Absolute Value

WARM UP

Plot each set of numbers on the number line and describe the relationship between the numbers.

1. 5 and −5
2. $2\frac{3}{4}$ and $-2\frac{3}{4}$
3. 8.634 and −8.634

LEARNING GOALS

- Explain the meaning of the absolute value of a rational number as its distance from 0 on a number line.
- Interpret the meaning of absolute value as the magnitude for a positive or negative quantity in a real-world context.
- Evaluate the absolute value of a quantity.
- Compare and order numbers expressed as absolute value and distinguish absolute value comparisons from statements about order.

KEY TERM

- absolute value

Numbers can be described by their distance from 0 on the number line. How can you use these distances to solve real-world problems?

Going the Distance

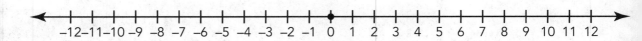

1. Plot a point at −7 on the number line.

2. Describe the distance from −7 to 0.

3. Plot as many other points as possible on the number line that are the same distance from 0 as −7.

4. How many numbers did you plot? Why do you think this is true?

Absolute Value as Magnitude

Let's revisit the number line from the *Human Number Line* lesson.

Your teacher will assign students to participate in the activity.
Be sure to record what happens on the number line.

- Student A: Stand on 0 and hold one end of the string provided by your teacher.

- Student B: Hold the other end of the string and stand on the number line as far as possible from Student A. Are there other places on the number line that you could stand and be as far from Student A as possible?

- Repeat this activity with two more pieces of string of different lengths and two additional students, Students C and D. Student A will hold the 0 end of each string.

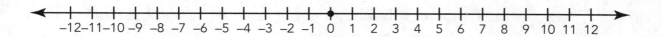

1. Compare the locations where each student stood.

   a. What do you notice about the distances each time the students moved?

   b. What do you notice about the approximate values for the numbers where each stood?

The magnitude, or **absolute value,** of a number is its distance from zero on a number line. The symbol for absolute value is | |. The expression |*n*| is read as "the absolute value of a number *n*."

Because distance cannot be negative, the absolute value of a number is always positive or 0.

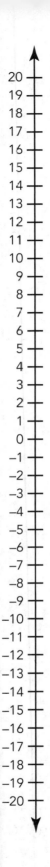

2. Plot 5 on the number line.

   a. How far is 5 from 0?   b. $|5|$ = _____

3. Plot −7.2 on the number line.

   a. How far is −7.2 from 0?   b. $|{-7.2}|$ = _____

4. Explain what each statement means. Name any other values that have the same absolute value, if possible.

   a. $|{-5}|$ b. $|1\frac{5}{6}|$

   c. $|0.75|$ d. $|{-1.36}|$

Use your investigation and a number line to answer each question.

5. Can two different numbers have the same absolute value? If so, provide examples.

6. What can you say about the absolute value of

   a. any positive number?

   b. any negative number?

   c. zero?

ACTIVITY 2.2
Interpreting Absolute Value Statements

Absolute values are used in real-world applications when you are interested in only the number and not in the sign of the number. When you look at temperature changes, you could say the temperature "fell by," "decreased by," or "increased by" an absolute value.

1. Complete the table with an appropriate situation, absolute value statement, and/or number. For the last row, assign the correct units to the number based on your situation.

Situation	Absolute Value Statement	Numeric Example (with units)
The temperature went from 55°F to 5°F.	The temperature fell by 50°F.	−50°F
The bank account balance went from $2500 to $2250.		
The bank account balance went from $495 to $615.		$120
	The water level increased by 4.9 feet.	
During the hike, the elevation went from 1125 feet to 1750 feet.		
		−10_____

You also use absolute value statements to describe how numbers compare with other numbers. You often use these statements without thinking about "less than" or "greater than." Rather, you use words like "debt," "lost," "colder," "depth," "above," "hotter," or "below."

2. Complete the table with an appropriate situation, absolute value statement, and/or example. For the last row, assign the correct units to the numeric example based on your situation.

Situation	Absolute Value Statement	Numeric Example (with units)
A water level less than $-2\frac{1}{2}$ feet	More than $2\frac{1}{2}$ feet below a full pool	−3 feet
An account balance less than −$30	A debt greater than $30	
A weight less than −7.5 pounds of previous weight	Lost more than 7.5 pounds	
A dive to a height less than −350 feet		
	Colder than 10 degrees below 0	
	A depth greater than 15 m	
	A golf tournament stroke total more than 7 strokes below par	
		−100_____

Par is the number of strokes, or swings, a golfer is expected to take.

1. In many buildings, particularly outside of the United States, the ground floor of a building is labeled as G or Lobby. The first floor of the building is one floor above the ground floor. The building pictured has a lobby, 10 floors of offices, and 4 floors of garage below the lobby.

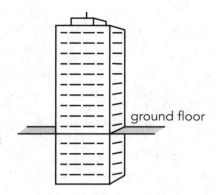

ground floor

a. Melanie has an office on the 9th floor and parks on the 3rd floor below the ground floor. Taylor and Cecelia are determining how many floors Melanie must go up from her car to reach her office.

Taylor represents the 9th floor as 9 and the 3rd floor below ground as −3. Therefore, since 9 − 3 = 6, Melanie traveled 6 floors to get from her car to her office.

Cecelia says that the ground floor to the 9th floor is 9 floors, and from the ground floor to the 3rd garage level is 3 floors. Melanie traveled $|9| + |−3| = 9 + 3 = 12$ floors.

Who is correct? Explain your reasoning.

Write a numeric expression using absolute values that would represent each situation. Then calculate the answer.

    b. Caleb parks his car on the 2nd floor below ground and works on the 7th floor. How many floors must he go up from his car to reach his office?

    c. Lucinda is working on the 8th floor. At lunch, she goes to her car on the 4th floor below ground, and then back up to the lobby. How many total floors does Lucinda travel?

    d. If Damon goes from his office on the 10th floor to a meeting on the 5th floor, how many floors does he travel and in which direction?

2. The Top Notch company's bank balances are shown. The table represents the first 10 weeks of operation. Overdrafts are represented by amounts within parentheses.

Week	1	2	3	4	5	6	7	8	9	10
Balance	$159.25	($201.35)	$231.57	($456.45)	($156)	($12.05)	$281.34	$175	$192.34	$213

    a. Use estimation to determine the gains/losses between consecutive weeks.

    b. Between which two weeks did Top Notch have the largest gain in money? What was the actual gain?

    c. Between which two weeks did Top Notch have the largest loss in money? What was the actual loss?

    d. What was the difference between the company's lowest balance and its highest balance?

e. Order the estimated gains and losses that you determined in part (a) from least to greatest. Use a negative sign to indicate losses.

f. Order the estimated gains and losses that you determined in part (a) from least to greatest according to their absolute values. What does the absolute value mean in the context of this problem?

g. Why are the orders different in parts (e) and (f)?

3. As part of a long-term science experiment, two rulers were connected at zero and used to measure the water level in a pond. The connected rulers were placed in the pond so that the water level aligned at zero. The water level was measured each week for 10 weeks.

Week	1	2	3	4	5	6	7	8	9	10
Water level	$2\frac{3}{4}$	$-2\frac{1}{8}$	$1\frac{7}{8}$	$-\frac{3}{4}$	$\frac{3}{4}$	$1\frac{1}{8}$	$-\frac{7}{8}$	$1\frac{1}{4}$	-2	$-\frac{3}{16}$

a. What do the positive numbers represent? What do the negative numbers represent?

b. Between which two weeks did the water level change the most? What was the change?

c. Between which two weeks did the water level change the least? What was the change?

d. How much did the water level change between Weeks 4 and 5? What was the change?

TALK the TALK

You Absolutely MUST Compare These!

Insert a >, <, or = symbol to make each statement true. Justify each answer in terms of the definition of absolute value and number lines.

1. $|-4.67|$ ___ $|3|$

2. $|-15|$ ___ $|15|$

3. $|25\frac{9}{10}|$ ___ $|-33\frac{2}{3}|$

4. $|13.45|$ ___ $|-27|$

5. $|-15.34|$ ___ $|-1\frac{11}{12}|$

6. $|-19\frac{1}{2}|$ ___ $|5.5|$

Assignment

Write

Explain the relationship between a number, its opposite, and its absolute value.

Remember

The absolute value of a rational number is its distance from zero on a number line. Absolute value equations can be used to calculate the distance between positive and negative numbers.

Practice

1. Julio is a wrestler for his high school wrestling team in the winter. Julio needs to stay around 140 pounds in the off-season. He charted his weight over the summer by listing the differences his weight was from 140 pounds. He uses negative numbers when his weight was under 140 pounds and positive numbers when his weight was above 140 pounds.

Week	1	2	3	4	5	6	7	8	9	10	11	12
Weight Difference	+4.5	+2.1	−1.5	−0.5	−2.5	+1.5	−3.75	−2.8	0	+1.3	−1.5	−5

   a. Was the amount his weight varied from 140 pounds in week 4 more or less than the amount it varied from 140 pounds in week 8?

   Insert a >, <, or = symbol to make the statement true. Explain your answer.

   $|{-0.5}|$ ◯ $|{-2.8}|$

   b. Was the amount his weight varied from 140 pounds in week 6 more or less than the amount it varied from 140 pounds in week 11?

   Insert a >, <, or = symbol to make the statement true. Explain your answer.

   $|{+1.5}|$ ◯ $|{-1.5}|$

   c. Use absolute values to determine the difference in Julio's weight from week 7 to week 10.

   d. Use absolute values to determine the difference in Julio's weight from week 8 to week 12.

2. The table shown tracks Julio's weight changes that he reports to his coach for the first 4 weeks of school. Complete the table to explain the changes.

Situation	Absolute Value Statement	Rational Number
His weight went from 140 to 135 pounds.	His weight fell by 5 pounds.	
His weight went from 135 pounds to 141 pounds.		6 lb
His weight went from 141 pounds to 140.5 pounds.		
His weight went from 140.5 pounds to 139 pounds.		

3. Weather experts collect many types of data to study and analyze, including extreme temperature changes. The interior West of North America experiences great temperature changes due to Chinook Winds. The table shows extreme temperature rises in three cities.

Place	Granville, ND	Fort Assiniboine, MT	Spearfish, SD
Date	Feb. 21, 1918	Jan. 19, 1892	Jan. 22, 1943
Time Period	12 hours	15 minutes	2 minutes
Temperature Change	From −33°F to 50°F	From −5°F to 37°F	From −4°F to 45°F

For each city, write an absolute value equation and use it to determine how much the temperature rose.

a. Granville, ND   b. Fort Assiniboine, MT   c. Spearfish, SD

4. Tyler measured the rainfall and evaporation using a rain gauge in his backyard for 8 days. Tyler marked his rain gauge with values from −6 inches to +6 inches and filled the gauge with water to the zero mark. For each question, write an expression using absolute value and then calculate the answer.

Days	1	2	3	4	5	6	7	8
Gauge Reading	0.5	−1.3	3.7	4.2	2.1	−0.9	−2.4	5.6

a. On how many days out of the eight did it rain?

b. Between which two consecutive readings did it rain the most? How many inches were recorded?

c. Between which two consecutive readings was evaporation the greatest? How many inches of water evaporated?

d. Calculate the gain or loss of water in the rain gauge between days 1 and 2. Express the change in the water level in the gauge as a positive or negative number.

e. Calculate the gain or loss of water in the rain gauge between days 2 and 3. Express the change in the water level in the gauge as a positive or negative number.

Stretch

Write a scenario to represent each rational number.

1. −12   2. −4$\frac{1}{2}$ 3. 7.3   4. −0.7

Review

1. Use the >, <, or = symbol to complete each statement.

   a. −5 $\bigcirc$ −8   b. −3 $\bigcirc$ 0   c. 5 $\bigcirc$ −5

2. Five employees work on the receiving dock at a factory. They divide the number of crates they unload from each truck equally. Define variables for the number of crates on a truck and for the number of crates each employee unloads from the truck. Write an equation that models the relationship between these variables.

3. Solve for the variable in each equation.

   a. $\frac{t}{2} = 15$ b. $y − 8 = 19$

What's in a Name?

Rational Number System

WARM UP

Represent each decimal or percent as a fraction in lowest terms.

a. 0.3

b. 2.8

c. $\frac{3}{4}$%

d. 212%

LEARNING GOALS

- Classify numbers according to their number systems.
- Apply and extend an understanding of whole numbers and integers to the system of rational numbers.
- Understand ordering of rational numbers.

KEY TERMS

- integers
- ellipsis
- rational numbers
- Density Property

You use many different types of numbers in math class and in the world, including whole numbers, fractions, and decimals, both positive and negative. How can you organize and classify different types of numbers?

Sort It Out!

Cut out the cards found at the end of the lesson. Then, analyze and sort the numbers into different groups. You may group them in any way you feel is appropriate, but you must sort the numbers into more than one group.

1. For each of your groups,

   - create a title that fits the numbers in that group.
   - list the numbers included.
   - write a rationale for why you group those particular numbers.

2. Compare your sort with your classmates' sorts. Create a list of the different ways your class grouped the numbers.

ACTIVITY 3.1

Analyzing Number Sorts

NOTES

1. Suzanne grouped these numbers together. Why do you think she put these numbers in the same group?

$$0, -452, 9, 24, |-3|, -3, -(-9), |-452|$$

2. Zane had a group similar to Suzanne's but he did not include −452 and −3. Why do think Zane omitted these numbers from his group?

3. Amelia said that she created two groups: Group 1 contains all the numbers that can be written as fractions and Group 2 contains all the numbers that cannot be written as fractions. Analyze Amelia's sorting idea.

   a. Which numbers do you think Amelia placed in Group 2?

   b. Justine is not sure about Amelia's sort. She thinks that all of the numbers can be written as fractions. Is Justine correct? Explain why or why not.

You have used different sets of numbers, including the set of natural, or counting, numbers and the set of whole numbers.

4. Identify the numbers from the sort that are in each set.

    a. natural numbers

    b. whole numbers

Notice the three periods before and after specific numbers in the set. These three periods are called an **ellipsis,** and they are used to represent infinity in a number set.

Throughout this topic, you have been learning about the set of *integers*. **Integers** are the set of whole numbers with their opposites. The integers can be represented by the set {..., −3, −2, −1, 0, 1, 2, 3, ...}.

5. Identify the numbers from the sort that are included in the set of integers.

You have also worked with rational numbers throughout this year. **Rational numbers** are the set of numbers that can be written as $\frac{a}{b}$, where a and b are integers and $b \neq 0$.

6. Identify the numbers from the sort that are included in the set of rational numbers.

Classifying Numbers

There are many ways you can classify numbers. As you saw in the previous activity, many of the classifications are subsets of other classifications. The diagram shows the different sets of numbers you have encountered in your mathematical experiences.

Natural numbers are a subset of whole numbers.

Whole numbers are a subset of integers.

Integers are a subset of rational numbers.

Pin the number on the bullseye! Your teacher will direct students to pin (or tape) a number card to its correct location in the diagram of the rational number set.

Rational

Integers

Whole

Natural

1. **For each value, check all of the number sets to which it belongs.**

Number	Natural Number	Whole Number	Integer	Rational Number
3				
3.222				
0				
−4.5				
$-\frac{3}{5}$				
54				
−5				
$\frac{23}{3}$				
0.667				
−1,364,698				

2. Complete the table with the missing examples and descriptions.

	Natural Numbers	Whole Numbers	Integers	Rational Numbers
Examples	1, 2, 3, ...		..., −3, −2, −1, 0, 1, 2, 3, ...	
Description	Counting numbers	Natural numbers and 0		

ACTIVITY 3.3 Density

The **Density Property** states that between any two rational numbers there is another rational number. The property is not true for natural numbers, whole numbers, or integers. For example, there is no integer between 25 and 26. There is no whole number or natural number between 12 and 13.

1. Plot the given rational numbers. Then plot and label a rational number between each pair of rational numbers.

   a. $4\frac{1}{3}$ and $4\frac{2}{3}$

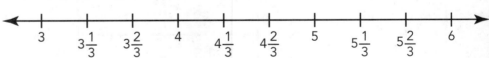

   b. 5.5 and 5.6

   c. 0.45 and 0.46

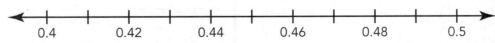

   d. −0.45 and −0.46

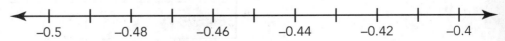

Complete each rational number line with a partner.

2. Create a number line from 0 to 1. Your goal is to plot and label a rational number closer to 1 than your partner.

Partner 1: Plot a rational number, A, between 0 and 1 that is close to 1.

Partner 2: Plot a rational number, B, between A and 1.

Repeat at least 2 more times.

3. Create a number line from −1 to 0. Your goal is to plot and label a rational number closer to 0 than your partner.

Partner 1: Plot a rational number, A, between −1 and 0 that is close to 0.

Partner 2: Plot a rational number, B, between A and 0.

Repeat at least 2 more times.

4. Create a number line from −6 to −5. Your goal is to plot and label a rational number closer to −5 than your partner.

Partner 1: Plot a rational number, A, between −6 and −5 that is close to −5.

Partner 2: Plot a rational number, B, between A and −5.

Repeat at least 2 more times.

TALK the TALK

Do They Always Belong?

Determine if each statement is true or false. Justify your answer using definitions and/or examples.

1. True   False   All whole numbers are rational numbers.

2. True   False   All rational numbers are whole numbers.

3. True   False   All rational numbers are integers.

4. True   False   All integers are rational numbers.

5. True   False   All whole numbers are integers.

6. True   False   All integers are whole numbers.

0	−5.78	$2\frac{15}{16}$	$\frac{3}{4}\%$	−452
$\frac{1}{2}$	24	9	$\frac{6}{7}$	$-\frac{6}{7}$
−0.5	0.5	$-\frac{1}{2}$	2.5%	5.78
−3	|−3|	$-\frac{2}{3}$	$\frac{1}{1000}$	0.001
−6.41	|6.41|	−(−9)	|−452|	−0.3
225%	$6\frac{1}{4}$	25%	0.25%	$\left\|\frac{215}{16}\right\|$

Assignment

Write

Define each term in your own words.

1. The set of rational numbers
2. The Density Property

Remember

Rational numbers include all numbers that can be written in the form $\frac{a}{b}$, where a and b are integers and b is not zero.

Practice

1. Write all the sets of numbers to which each value belongs.

   a. The tundra covers about $\frac{1}{5}$ of Earth's surface.

   b. The average annual temperature is $-18°$ Fahrenheit.

   c. There are 48 varieties of land mammals found in the tundra region.

   d. The permafrost is a layer of frozen soil that is located below Earth's surface at -1476 feet.

   e. During the summer months, the low temperature averages about $37.4°$ F.

2. Nadine collects data about some animals. Determine a rational number between each pair of rational numbers. Plot all three numbers on a number line.

   a. A mole's runway is between -3 and -12 inches in the ground.

   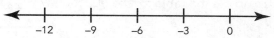

   b. The musky rat kangaroo weighs between $\frac{3}{4}$ and $\frac{3}{2}$ pound.

   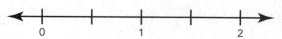

   c. The percent of change of the Alaskan polar bear population in the past year was between -0.33 and -0.32.

   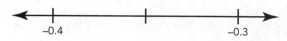

Stretch

Are there more integers or more natural numbers? Even though there are infinitely many of both, it seems like there should be more integers than natural numbers. But, actually, there are just as many integers as there are natural numbers!

If you can show how to assign an integer to every natural number, you will demonstrate that the two sets of numbers are equal. How do you think this can be done?

Review

1. Write an absolute value expression to calculate the answer to each question.

   a. The temperature at 9:00 A.M. was 40°. The temperature at 2:00 P.M. was −10°. What was the change in temperature?

   b. You began your hike at 30 feet below sea level. You are now at 200 feet. How far have you hiked?

2. Complete the table for the equation $w = \frac{m}{9.2}$.

m	w
27.6	
	5
74.52	
92	
	14

3. Plot each ordered pair on a coordinate plane.

   a. (2, 4)

   b. (5.5, 1.75)

   c. $(4\frac{2}{5}, 5\frac{4}{5})$

Signed Numbers Summary

KEY TERMS

- negative numbers
- infinity
- absolute value
- integers
- ellipsis
- rational numbers
- Density Property

LESSON 1

Human Number Line

A number line can be created by reflecting the positive numbers across zero. The values to the left of zero on the number line are called **negative numbers** and are labeled with a negative sign. You can write a positive number with a positive sign or without any sign. For example, positive 5 can be written as +5 or 5.

The positive values extend to positive infinity, and the negative numbers extend to negative infinity. **Infinity**, represented by the symbol ∞, means a quantity with no end or bound.

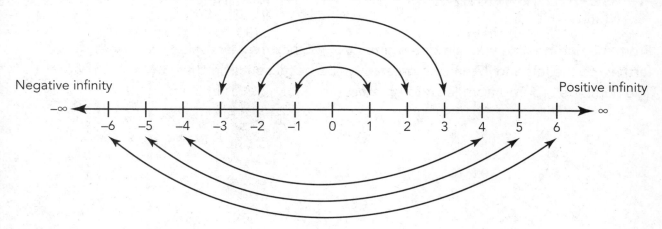

Opposite numbers are reflections of each other across 0 on the number line.

- The opposite of a positive number is a corresponding negative number.
- The opposite of a negative number is a corresponding positive number.

Attaching a negative sign to a number means reflecting that number across zero on the number line. The number 0 is the only number that doesn't have an opposite.

For example, the numbers $6\frac{1}{2}$, −13, −18.5, and their opposites are plotted on the number line.

Number lines can also be vertical, like a thermometer or a measure of elevation.

You can use a thermometer to plot temperatures and to compare and order temperatures. In vertical number lines like this one, the greater the value, the higher up on the number line.

For example, compare 40 degrees to −60 degrees. By plotting each temperature on the thermometer, you can see that 40 degrees is above −60 degrees. Therefore 40 > −60.

You can compare different types of numbers by plotting the numbers on a number line.

For example, the numbers, $-6\frac{2}{3}$, 10.5, −25, 17, and 0 have been plotted on the number line. Use the number line to order the values from least to greatest.

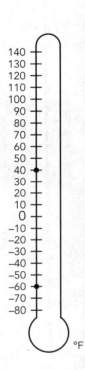

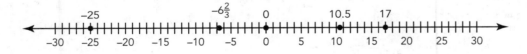

From the number line you can determine that −25 has the least value because it is the farthest to the left and 17 has the greatest value because it is farthest to the right. The numbers ordered from least to greatest are −25, $-6\frac{2}{3}$, 0, 10.5, and 17.

Magnificent Magnitude

The magnitude, or **absolute value**, of a number is its distance from zero on a number line. The symbol for absolute value is | |. The expression |n| is read as "the absolute value of a number n." Because distance cannot be negative, the absolute value of a number is always positive or 0.

|9| = 9, because 9 is 9 units from 0 on a number line.
|−3.8| = 3.8, because −3.8 is 3.8 units from 0 on a number line.

Absolute values are used in real-world applications when you are interested in only the number and not in the sign of the number. You also use absolute value statements to describe how numbers compare with other numbers.

Situation	Absolute Value Statement	Numeric Example
The temperature went from 55°F to 5°F.	The temperature fell by 50°F.	−50°F
The bank account balance went from $550 to $795.	The balance increased by $245.	$245
A water level went from 10.3 feet to 6.7 feet.	A water level fell by 3.6 feet.	−3.6 feet
A water level less than $-2\frac{1}{2}$ feet	More than $2\frac{1}{2}$ feet below a full pool	−3 feet
A temperature less than −5° F	Colder than 5°F below 0	−8°F
An account balance less than −$100	A debt greater than $100	−$110

Absolute value equations can be used to calculate the distance between positive and negative numbers to solve real-world problems.

For example, the Top Notch company's bank balances are shown. The table shown represents the first 10 weeks of operation. Overdrafts, which are a negative balance, are represented by amounts within parentheses. What was the gain or loss between Weeks 2 and 3?

Week	1	2	3	4	5	6	7	8	9	10
Balance	$159.25	($201.35)	$231.57	($456.45)	($156)	($12.05)	$281.34	$175	$192.34	$213

At the end of Week 2, the company had a negative balance of $201.35 and at the end of Week 3 it had a positive balance of $231.57. The company had a gain between these two weeks because it went from a lesser balance to a greater balance. The gain is equal to the sum of the absolute values of the two balances.

$$|-\$201.35| + |\$231.57| = \$201.35 + \$231.57 = \$432.92$$

LESSON

3

What's In a Name?

Integers are the set of whole numbers with their opposites. The integers can be represented by the set $\{\ldots, -3, -2, -1, 0, 1, 2, 3, \ldots\}$. The three periods before and after the numbers in the set are called an **ellipsis**, and they are used to represent infinity in a number set.

Rational numbers are the set of numbers that can be written as $\frac{a}{b}$, where a and b are integers and b does not equal 0.

There are many ways you can classify numbers. Many of the classifications are subsets of other classifications. The diagram shows the different sets of numbers you have encountered in your mathematical experiences.

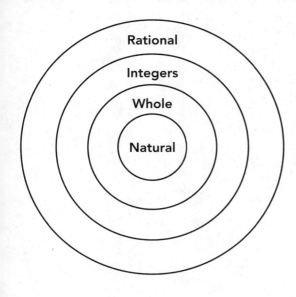

Natural numbers are a subset of whole numbers.

Whole numbers are a subset of integers.

Integers are a subset of rational numbers.

The number 2 is a rational number, an integer, a whole number, and a natural number.

The number 0 is a rational number, an integer, and a whole number.

The number −11 is a rational number and an integer.

The numbers 12.5 and $-\frac{3}{4}$ are both rational numbers.

The **Density Property** states that between any two rational numbers there is another rational number.

For example, consider the rational numbers −0.42 and −0.43 and the number line shown. The number represented by point A is another rational number that falls between −0.42 and −0.43 such that −0.43 < A < −0.42. Point A could represent the value −0.425.

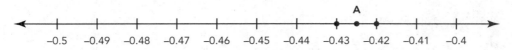

The property is not true for natural numbers, whole numbers, or integers. For example, there is no integer between −25 and −26. There is no whole number or natural number between 12 and 13.

TOPIC 2
The Four Quadrants

Air traffic controllers use radar to track tens of thousands of commercial airline flights every day. Controllers use quadrants to identify the locations, altitudes, and speeds of the many different flights.

Module 4: Moving Beyond Positive Quantities

TOPIC 2: THE FOUR QUADRANTS

In this topic, students explore the four quadrant coordinate plane. They use reflections of the first quadrant on patty paper and their knowledge of the rational number line to build their own four quadrant coordinate plane. Students look for patterns in the signs of the ordered pairs in each quadrant and the ordered pairs that lie along the vertical and horizontal axes. After developing a strong foundation for plotting points and determining distances on the coordinate plane, students analyze and solve problems involving geometric shapes on the coordinate plane. They use the knowledge gained throughout the course to solve a wide range of problems on the coordinate plane, using scenarios, graphs, equations, and tables.

Where have we been?

Prior to grade 6, students represented real-world and mathematical problems in the first quadrant of a coordinate plane and interpreted the coordinate values of points. In the previous topic, students extended the rational number line to include negative values. The opening activities of this topic access all of this prior knowledge as students construct the four quadrant coordinate plane.

Where are we going?

This topic provides students with an introduction to the entire real number coordinate plane. Throughout the rest of this course and in the coming years, students will represent relationships on the coordinate plane and interpret the meanings of points, lines, and other graph elements plotted on the plane. This topic provides the foundation for those lessons.

The Four-Quadrant Coordinate Plane

The intersection of a horizontal x-axis and vertical y-axis at a point called the origin divides an infinite flat plane into four quadrants.

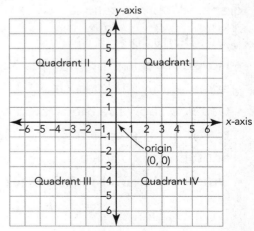

Myth: "I'm not smart."

The word "smart" is tricky because it means different things to different people. For example, would you say a baby is "smart"? On the one hand, a baby is helpless and doesn't know anything. But on the other hand, a baby is insanely smart because she is constantly learning new things every day.

This example is meant to demonstrate that "smart" can have two meanings. It can mean "the knowledge that you have," or it can mean "the capacity to learn from experience." When someone says he or she is "not smart," are they saying they do not have much knowledge, or are they saying they lack the capacity to learn? If it's the first definition, then none of us are smart until we acquire that information. If it's the second definition, then we know that is completely untrue because *everyone* has the capacity to grow as a result of new experiences.

So, if your student doesn't think that they are smart, encourage them to be patient. They have the capacity to learn new facts and skills. It might not be easy, and it will take some time and effort. But the brain is automatically wired to learn. Smart should not refer only to how much knowledge you currently have.

#mathmythbusted

Talking Points

You can further support your student's learning by asking questions about the work they do in class or at home. Your student is learning to use an expanded number system in different contexts and with different graphical representations.

Questions to Ask

- How does this problem look like something you did in class?
- Can you show me the strategy you used to solve this problem? Do you know another way to solve it?
- Does your answer make sense? Why?

Key Terms

quadrants
The four regions on the coordinate plane are called quadrants. They are numbered with Roman numerals from one to four (I, II, III, IV) starting in the upper right-hand quadrant and moving counterclockwise.

ordered pairs
An ordered pair is a pair of numbers that can be represented as (x, y) to indicate the position of a point on the coordinate plane. For example, the ordered pair for the origin is $(0, 0)$.

Four Is Better Than One

1

Extending the Coordinate Plane

WARM UP
Plot each point.

A (3, 5)   *B* (0, 4)   *C* (6, 1)   *D* (8, 0)   *E* (0, 0)

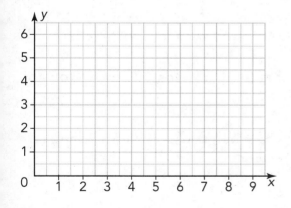

LEARNING GOALS
- Identify the four quadrants of the coordinate plane and the characteristics of points located in each.
- Locate and plot ordered pairs of positive and negative rational numbers on the coordinate plane.
- Determine the relationship between the signs of coordinates of ordered pairs that are reflections across one or both axes.
- Use absolute value to determine distances on the coordinate plane.
- Solve real-world and mathematical problems by graphing points in all four quadrants of the coordinate plane.

KEY TERM
- quadrants

You can locate and plot ordered pairs of positive numbers on a coordinate plane. How can you extend the plane to include ordered pairs of any rational numbers?

All About Extending

Consider the coordinate plane that you have used to graph points where both the *x*- and *y*-coordinates were zero or positive numbers.

1. Based on what you have learned about number lines:

   a. What do you know about the number line that makes up the *x*-axis? Extend that number line and label it appropriately.

   b. What do you know about the number line that makes up the *y*-axis? Extend that number line and label it appropriately.

2. The point where the *x*-axis and *y*-axis intersect is known as the origin. Label the point of intersection with its coordinates.

By extending the number lines that form the axes, you have created the entire coordinate plane.

3. How many regions are created when the coordinate plane is extended to all rational numbers?

The coordinate plane is often called the Cartesian coordinate plane, named for René Descartes.

The regions on the coordinate plane are called **quadrants**. They are numbered with Roman numerals from one to four (I, II, III, IV) starting in the upper right-hand quadrant and moving counterclockwise.

4. Label each of the quadrants on your coordinate plane.

Human Coordinate Plane

Your teacher is going to direct students to stand at certain locations on the human coordinate plane.

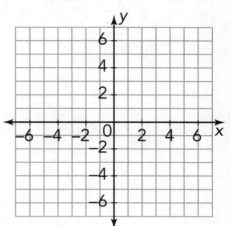

1. For each student, plot and label the point where the student is standing on the coordinate plane. Then record the coordinates of that point in the table.

Student	Location	Student	Location
A		H	
B		I	
C		J	
D		K	
E		L	
F		M	
G		N	

> Help each other decide how to plot the ordered pairs.

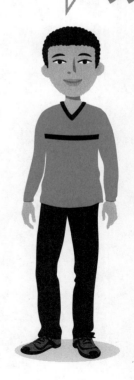

2. Where did each student always start? How did each student know which direction to go first?

3. What do you notice about the coordinates of the points that are in the same quadrant of the coordinate plane?

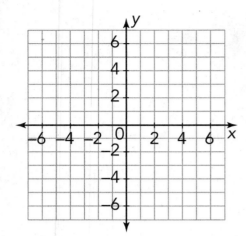

Your teacher is going to select students to plot ordered pairs that meet specific conditions. The students will select locations that satisfy those conditions.

4. For each student, plot and label the point where the student is standing on the coordinate plane. Then record the coordinates of that point in the table.

Student	Condition	Location
A	Anywhere	
B	Negative x-coordinate	
C	Negative y-coordinate	
D	On an axis	
E	In QII	
F	In QIII	

5. Compare the ordered pairs you have plotted and identified in this activity. What is similar about the points you graphed in each region or axis of the graph?

a. QI:

b. QII:

c. QIII:

d. QIV:

e. x-axis:

f. y-axis:

Investigating Reflections

In this activity, you will use patty paper to search for specific patterns on the coordinate plane.

Reflecting across the x-axis: Place a sheet of patty paper over the coordinate plane and trace the axes.

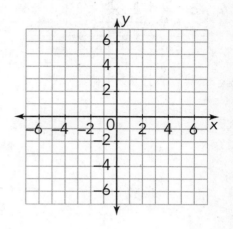

1. For each ordered pair,

   • Plot and label the point on patty paper.
   • Fold the patty paper on the x-axis.
   • Trace the point through the patty paper.
   • Label the coordinates of the new point.

   a. A (4, 1)   A′ (____ , ____)

   b. B (−3, 4)   B′ (____ , ____)

   c. C (5, −2)   C′ (____ , ____)

   d. D (0, −7)   D′ (____ , ____)

A′ is read "A prime."

2. What did you notice about the coordinates of the original points and their reflections? Write a generalization for how the coordinates of a point and its reflection across the x-axis are related.

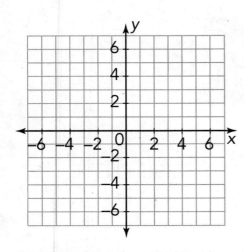

Now let's investigate reflecting across the y-axis. Place a new sheet of patty paper over the coordinate plane and trace the axes.

3. For each ordered pair,

   • Plot and label the point on patty paper.
   • Fold the patty paper on the y-axis.
   • Trace the point through the patty paper.
   • Label the coordinates of the new point.

   a. A (4, 1)   A' (____ , ____)

   b. B (−3, 4)   B' (____ , ____)

   c. C (5, −2)   C' (____ , ____)

   d. D (−3, 0)   D' (____ , ____)

4. What did you notice about the coordinates of the original points and their reflections? Write a generalization for how the coordinates of a point and its reflection across the y-axis are related.

Your teacher is going to select students to plot ordered pairs that meet specific conditions. The students will select locations that satisfy those conditions.

5. For each student, plot and label the point where the student is standing on the coordinate plane. Then record the coordinates of that point in the table.

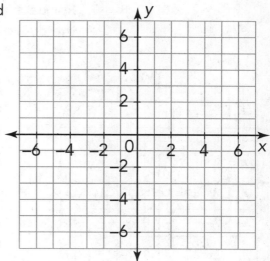

Student	Condition	Location
A	Quadrant II	
B	Reflection of A across the x-axis	
C	Reflection of B across the y-axis	

6. Compare the ordered pairs for A and C. What do you notice about their coordinates? Write a generalization for how the coordinates of a point and its reflection across both axes are related.

7. For each pair of conditions, plot and label two points. Record the coordinates of the points.

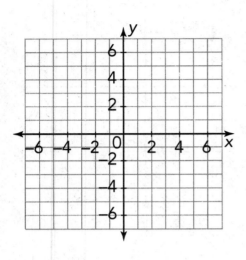

a. One point is in Quadrant II. The two points are reflections of each other across the x-axis.

b. One point is in Quadrant III. The points are reflections of each other across the y-axis.

c. One point is in Quadrant IV. The points are reflections of each other across both axes.

8. In general, how are points that are reflections across one or both axes similar to and different from each other?

Horizontal and Vertical Distance on the Coordinate Plane

1. Consider points A and B.

    a. Use the coordinate plane to determine the distance from point A to point B.

    b. Describe how the coordinates of points A and B are similar.

    c. Write an absolute value equation using the x-coordinates of the points to calculate the distance.

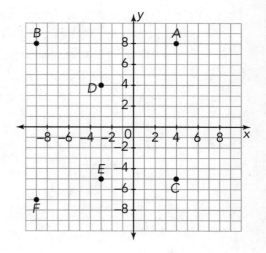

2. Consider points B and F.

    a. Use the coordinate plane to determine the distance from point B to point F.

    b. Describe how the coordinates of points B and F are similar.

    c. Write an absolute value equation using the y-coordinates of the points to calculate the distance.

3. Write an absolute value equation and calculate the distance from:

    a. point D to (−3, −5).

    b. (−7, −4) to (3, −4).

    c. (6, 2) to (6, −5).

    d. point B to (−9, 2).

    e. (8, −7) to point F.

ACTIVITY 1.4   T-Rex Dig

In the T-Rex Dig game, players place the "bones" of their dinosaur horizontally or vertically on a coordinate grid. Players then take turns guessing the location of each other's dino bones using coordinates. Once a player has located all of the other player's dino bones, the game is over.

Let's look at a sample game board and questions that might be asked to uncover all the dino bones.

1. **Use the game board to answer questions about the T-Rex fossils. (Each grid line is 1 foot long.)**

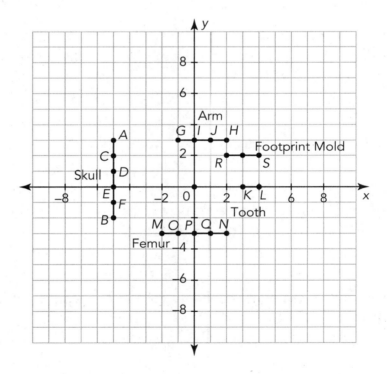

   a. **How long is the T-Rex's skull? Write an absolute value equation to justify your answer.**

b. How many coordinates must be guessed to completely "uncover" the skull?

c. How long is the T-Rex's femur? Write an absolute value equation to justify your answer.

d. What is the greatest number of quadrants crossed by any one fossil?

e. Are any fossils on an axis? If so, identify the axis, the fossil, and the coordinates of the fossil(s).

2. Your turn! Use the graph paper provided at the end of the lesson. Use the bottom grid to plot and label your 5 fossils. You may want to label some of the coordinates to help you as you play the game. Use the top grid to record the coordinates you ask of your partner.

As you play the game ask your opponent mathematical questions. For example, you can ask:

- Is the femur symmetric over an axis?
- How many of your fossils are vertical?
- Are any of the fossils on an axis? (But you can't ask which axis!)
- Do any of the fossils share an ending x-coordinate with another fossil?

TALK the TALK

Determining Coordinates

Use the graph and information provided to answer each question.

- The graph shows the locations of point *F* and point *G*.

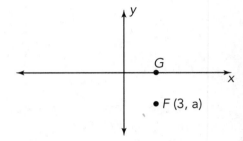

- Point *G* is on the *x*-axis and has the same *x*-coordinate as point *F*.

- Point *H* is located at (−4, *a*).

- The distance from point *F* to point *G* is half the distance from point *F* to point *H*.

1. **What is the value of *a*? Explain how you determined this coordinate.**

2. **Plot point *J* so that the distance from point *F* to point *J* is the same as the distance from point *F* to point *H*. Explain how you decided where to plot point *J*.**

T-Rex Dig Game Board

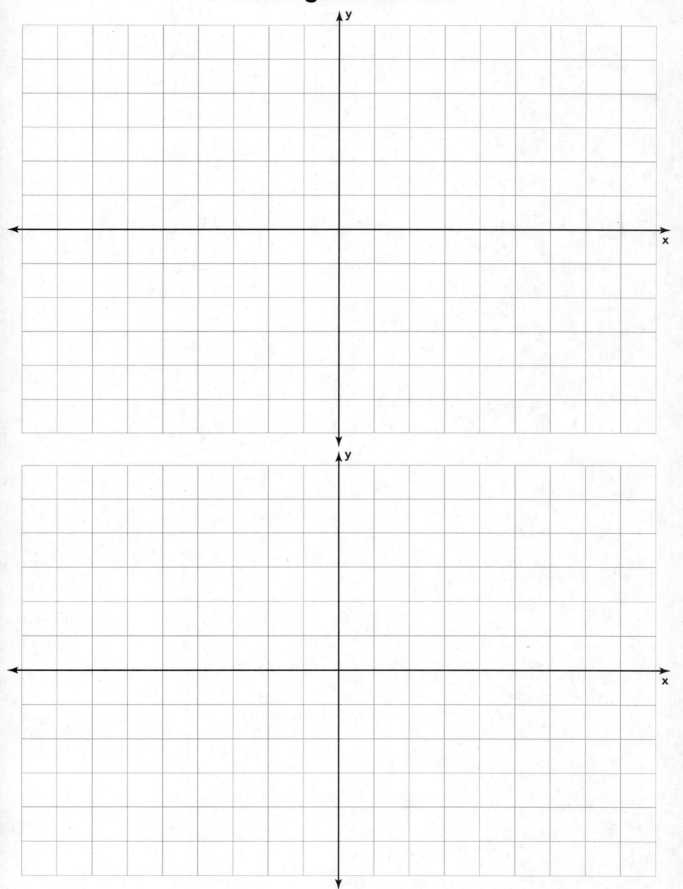

Assignment

Write

Use the terms **axis**, **quadrant**, and **coordinates** to explain how ordered pairs that differ only by sign are related to each other.

Remember

The Cartesian coordinate plane is formed by two perpendicular number lines that intersect at the zeros, or the origin. The intersecting number lines divide the plane into four regions, called quadrants.

Practice

1. Identify the ordered pair associated with each point graphed on the coordinate plane.

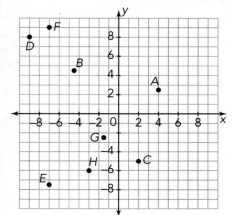

2. Plot and label the locations of points P through Z on a coordinate plane. Draw line segments from point to point, beginning and ending at point P. Describe the resulting figure.

   P (0, 5) Q (1, 3) R (4, 3)

   S (2, 1) T (4, −3) V (0, −1)

   W (−4, −3) X (−2, 1) Y (−4, 3)

   Z (−1, 3)

3. Plot the ordered pair (a, b) in Quadrant I of a coordinate plane and the ordered pair (c, d) in Quadrant III. Plot and label each additional ordered pair. Explain how you knew where to plot each point.
   a. (−a, b)   b. (a, −b)   c. (−a, −b)   d. (−c, d)   e. (c, −d)   f. (−c, −d)

4. The coordinate plane shown represents a map of Paul's neighborhood. Each square represents one city block. Paul's house is located at point A, which is the origin. The other points represent the following locations.

   B – USA Bank   C – Paul's friend Franco's house
   D – Gray's Grocery Store   E – Post Office
   F – Edward Middle School   G – Playground
   H – Smiles Orthodontics

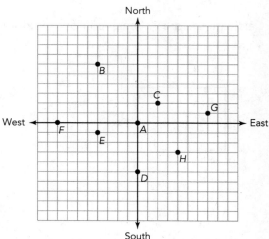

5. Explain how Paul can get to the given destination from his house if he were to first walk east or west and then walk north or south. Then, determine the coordinates of the destination point and the quadrant in which the point is located.
   a. USA Bank   b. Smiles Orthodontics
   c. Franco's house   d. Playground
   e. Post Office

6. Identify the ordered pairs associated with B and E. Describe how the ordered pairs are similar.

7. Write an absolute value equation using the y-coordinates of the points to calculate the distance between B and E.

8. How can an absolute value equation help you calculate the distance from one point to another on the coordinate plane when the points are on the same vertical or horizontal line?

Stretch

Create a rectangle ABCD on a coordinate plane that meets the following conditions:

- all four points are in different quadrants
- point A is in Quadrant II with coordinates $(-a, b)$
- the distance from point A to point B is $3a$
- the distance from point A to point D is $4b$
- neither axis is a line of symmetry in the rectangle

Review

Determine two rational numbers that are between the two given rational numbers.

1. 3.4 and 3.5
2. $\frac{12}{5}$ and $\frac{13}{5}$

State the opposite of each number and plot both numbers on a number line.

3. $2\frac{1}{8}$
4. -5.97

Calculate the area of each composite figure.

5.

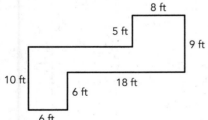

6.

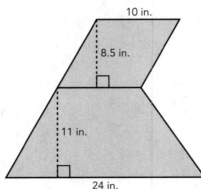

It's a Bird, It's a Plane ... It's a Polygon on the Plane!

Graphing Geometric Figures

WARM UP

1. Draw a rectangle that is not a square.

2. Draw a rhombus that is also a rectangle.

3. Draw a trapezoid that is not a parallelogram.

LEARNING GOALS

- Plot points in all four quadrants to form polygons.
- Draw polygons in the coordinate plane using coordinates for the vertices.
- Determine the area enclosed by a polygon on the coordinate plane.
- Use coordinates to determine the length of a side joining points with the same first or second coordinate.
- Solve real-world and mathematical problems with geometric shapes in all four quadrants on the coordinate plane.

You have determined area and perimeter of common polygons. You have decomposed complex figures into simpler shapes to determine their area. You have also determined the volume of right rectangular prisms. How can you use the coordinate plane to determine the area, perimeter, and even volume of shapes and objects?

Shape Up!

Your teacher will select students to participate in the activity and provide them with conditions to plot on the Human Coordinate Plane.

1. For each student, plot and label the point where the student is standing on the coordinate plane. Use a different color for each location. Then record the coordinates of the point where the student is standing in the table.

Student	Location 1	Location 2	Location 3
A			
B			
C			
D			

2. What shape did your classmates form at Location 1? How can you prove that they formed the given shape?

3. Record the shape formed at Location 2. Prove that your classmates formed the shape.

4. Record the shape formed at Location 3. Prove that your classmates formed the shape.

What Shape Am I?

One advantage of the Cartesian coordinate plane is that it enables mathematicians to use coordinates to analyze geometric figures.

1. Graph the points on the coordinate plane, and connect the points to form a polygon.

x	y
1	−2
−5	−2
1	3
−5	3

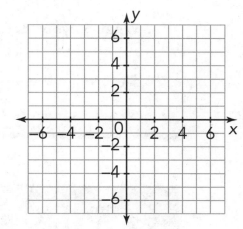

   a. Identify the polygon formed and justify your answer.

   b. Determine the perimeter of the polygon.

   c. Determine the area of the polygon.

2. Graph the points on the plane, and connect the points to form a polygon.

x	y
−2	3
3	−2
−2	−3
3	2

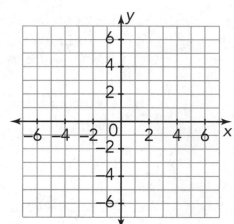

   a. What polygon is formed? Justify your answer.

   b. Determine the area of the polygon.

3. Graph the points on the plane, and connect the points to form a polygon.

x	y
−2	5
3	−3
−2	−3
5	2

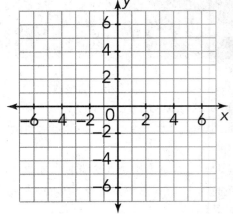

a. What polygon is formed? Justify your answer.

b. Determine the area of the polygon.

ACTIVITY
2.2

Completing Polygons on the Plane

Remember, a parallelogram is a quadrilateral in which both pairs of opposite sides are parallel.

1. The points A (−2, 4) and B (−2, −2) are plotted on the coordinate plane shown.

a. Plot and label points C, D, E, and F so that squares ABCD and ABEF are formed.

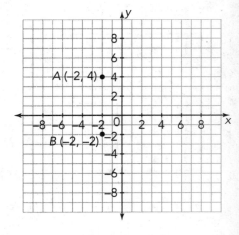

b. Determine the area of each square.

c. Compare your squares with your classmates' squares. Are all the squares the same or different? How do you know that the squares are drawn correctly?

2. On the coordinate plane, the line segment *AB* is graphed.

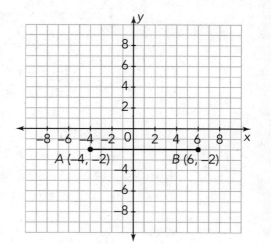

a. Plot and label points *C* and *D* to form parallelogram *ABCD* with a height of 4 units.

b. Determine the area of your parallelogram.

c. Compare your parallelogram with your classmates' parallelograms. Are all the parallelograms the same or different? How do you know that the parallelograms are drawn correctly?

3. On the coordinate plane, the points *A* (−3, −3) and *B* (4, −3) are plotted to form segment *AB*.

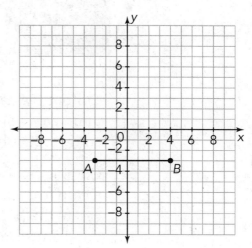

a. Plot and label point *C* so that a right triangle is formed.

b. Plot and label point *D* so that an acute triangle is formed.

c. Determine the areas of your triangles.

d. Compare your triangles with your classmates' triangles. Are all the triangles the same or different? How do you know that the triangles are drawn correctly?

4. On the coordinate plane, points A and B are plotted to form segment AB.

a. Plot and label two points to form trapezoid ABCD with a height of 5 units. Your trapezoid should cross into at least 3 quadrants.

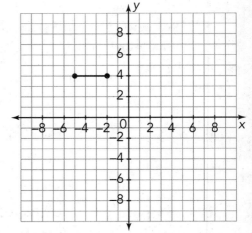

b. Determine the area of your trapezoid.

c. Compare your trapezoid with your classmates' trapezoids. Are all the trapezoids the same or different? How do you know that the trapezoids are drawn correctly?

ACTIVITY
2.3

Creating Polygons on the Plane

Cut out the cards and the grid at the end of the lesson. There are three types of cards: Number of Quadrants, Polygon, Area. Keep the cards separate but shuffle each stack and place them face down.

Complete this activity with a partner. One partner should draw a card from each stack. Based on the cards, each partner must create the polygon named, across the number of quadrants on the quadrants card, with the area from the area card. The first person to correctly complete the task gets a point. Partners should check each other's work. The first partner to 5 points wins the game.

If the partner is unable to form the shape using the given conditions because it is not possible or the student cannot meet the conditions, that partner loses their turn.

Record your polygons on the grid paper provided.

Outfitting a Playground

You have been asked to advise on the design of a playground for your local elementary school. The playground is laid out in a grid with a unit of 1 foot and a merry-go-round at the center of the playground. Your project is to determine the amount of sand needed for the fossil dig sandbox and the sand pit under the swing set.

The coordinates for the fossil pit are (−18, −7), (−10, −7), (−18, −13), and (−10, −13).

1. Determine the volume of the fossil pit if the pit is 0.75 feet deep.

2. If the school will fill the pit halfway up with sand, determine the volume of sand that is required.

3. Each 50-pound bag of sand holds about 0.5 cubic feet of sand. Determine the number of bags of sand needed for the fossil pit.

4. Each bag of sand costs $3.80. How much will the sand cost for the fossil pit?

The coordinates for the swing set sand pit are (15, 2), (40, 2), (15, −8), and (40, −8).

5. Determine the volume of the swing set sand pit if the pit is 0.5 feet deep.

6. If the school has $250 to spend on sand for the swing set sand pit, how much of it can be filled with sand?

TALK the TALK

Introduction to Coordinate Proof

1. The coordinates of a parallelogram are given. Segment *AB* is parallel to the *x*-axis.

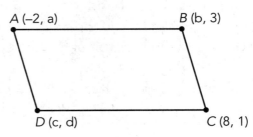

a. Determine the values for *a*, *b*, *c*, and *d*, if possible.

b. Write an expression for the length of segment *AB*.

c. Determine the vertical height of the parallelogram.

d. Write an expression for the area of the parallelogram.

e. If $b = 5$, determine the values for *a*, *c*, and *d*. Then calculate the area of the parallelogram.

Number of Quadrants, Polygon Names, and Area Measurements

1 Quadrant	2 Quadrants	3 Quadrants	4 Quadrants
Square	Rectangle	Triangle	Trapezoid
Any Parallelogram	Any Quadrilateral	Any Polygon	Rhombus
18 square units	16 square units	20 square units	24 square units
30 square units	36 square units	15 square units	50 square units

Assignment

Write

Explain how to use the coordinate plane and absolute value to determine perimeter and area of geometric shapes.

Remember

One advantage of the Cartesian coordinate plane is that it enables mathematicians to use coordinates to analyze geometric figures. The distance between two points on a coordinate plane can be calculated by using the coordinates of the two points.

Practice

1. Create and analyze a trapezoid.

   a. Plot and label four points on a coordinate plane that satisfy all the conditions listed:

      - Each point is in a different quadrant.
      - The four points form a trapezoid with only one pair of parallel sides.
      - The trapezoid has a height of 9 units.
      - One base of the trapezoid has a length of 6 units.
      - The second base of the trapezoid has a length of 3 units.
      - None of the points are located on an axis.
      - The trapezoid is not symmetric to either axis.

   b. Determine the area of the trapezoid.

   c. Is it possible to create a trapezoid that satisfies the conditions but has a different area? Explain.

2. Plot and identify four points across at least 2 quadrants that form a parallelogram that is not a rectangle. Determine the area of the parallelogram.

3. Plot and identify four points across at least 3 quadrants that form a non-square rectangle. Determine the area of the rectangle.

Stretch

Pick's Theorem says that the area of a polygon that has its vertices on a lattice—a field of evenly spaced points—can be calculated as follows:

- Count the number of interior points.
- Add this to half the number of boundary points (circled).
- Subtract 1.

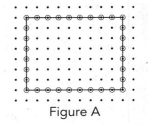

Figure A

1. Determine the area of Figure A using Pick's Theorem.
2. The coordinate plane can be like a lattice of points. How can you use this fact to determine the area of the given square?
3. Demonstrate Pick's Theorem on the coordinate plane using other polygons drawn in all four quadrants.

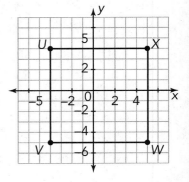

Review

1. Calculate the distance of each number from 125. Use positive numbers to indicate the distance when the number is greater than 125 and negative numbers to indicate the distance when the number is less than 125.
   a. 107
   b. 161
   c. 87
   d. 232

2. Graph the solution set for each given inequality.
   a. $x > 7.75$
   b. $x \le \dfrac{5}{2}$

There Are Many Paths...

Problem Solving on the Coordinate Plane

WARM UP

Solve each equation.

1. $120 + h = 315$

2. $w - 17 = 38$

3. $\frac{c}{5} = 12$

4. $169 = 13w$

LEARNING GOALS

- Solve real-world and mathematical problems by graphing points in all four quadrants of the coordinate plane.
- Interpret the meaning of points plotted on the coordinate plane.
- Use equations to solve real-world problems.
- Use graphs relating an independent and dependent quantity changing in relationship to one another to solve real-world problems.
- List advantages and disadvantages of different representations for solving real-world and mathematical problems on the coordinate plane.

Now that you understand how to plot points in all four quadrants of the coordinate plane, you can solve many more types of problems than you could previously. How can you use graphs and equations to solve problems?

Emma's Birthday

Analyze the graph.

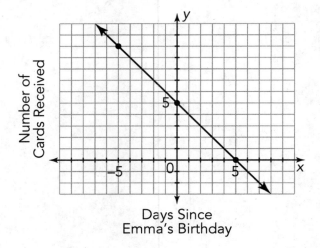

1. Explain what you can determine about the situation from the graph.

2. What do the plotted points mean in terms of this situation?

3. Do all of the values on the line make sense in terms of the situation?

4. Can you determine an equation for the graph?

Weigh In

Julio is a wrestler for his high school team. Although he does not wrestle during the 12 weeks of summer, his coach would like him to stay around 140 pounds so that he doesn't have to work so hard during the season to stay in his 142-pound weight class. Julio charted his weight over the summer.

Week	1	2	3	4	5	6	7	8	9	10	11	12
Weight	144.5	142.1	138.5	139.5	137.5	141.5	136.25	137.2	140	141.3	138.5	135
Weight Differential												

1. Consider the table shown.

   a. Which quantity is the independent quantity and which is the dependent? Explain your reasoning.

   b. What is the unit for each quantity?

   c. Which quadrant(s) will you need in order to plot Julio's data? Draw and label your axes. Then graph the data.

2. The coach was impressed with Julio's data collection, but he was interested in how much Julio's weight varied from 140 pounds each week.

   a. Complete the last row of weight differentials, the differences of Julio's weight from 140 pounds. Use negative numbers when the weight is below 140 pounds and positive numbers when his weight is above 140 pounds.

   b. What is the dependent quantity in this situation?

   c. Which quadrant(s) will you need in order to plot Julio's data for the coach's request? Draw and label your axes, including the units. Then graph the data.

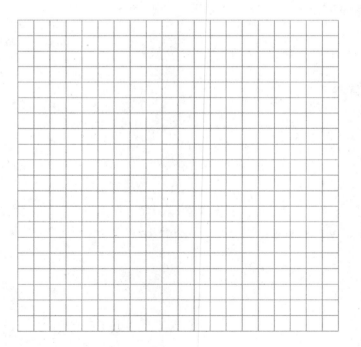

3. Compare the two approaches taken by Julio and his coach.

   a. Compare the independent and dependent quantities.

   b. Compare the graphs. What do you notice about the patterns of the points?

   c. Explain the meaning of the x-axis in each approach.

   d. Why do you think the coach preferred his approach over Julio's approach?

4. Use the table and graphs to answer each question.

   a. Between which two consecutive weeks did Julio's weight change the most? What was the weight change?

   b. What is the difference between Julio's highest weight and his lowest weight?

   c. Which representation—table, Julio's graph, the coach's graph—did you use to answer the questions? Why did you make those choices?

   d. If you were Julio's coach, what advice would you give Julio?

An interesting day of temperature changes occurred in Rapid City, South Dakota, on January 22, 1943. The table shows the temperature changes that happened throughout the day.

Time	Temperature (°C)
10:30 A.M.	−6.7
10:35 A.M.	13.3
12:00 P.M.	15.6
12:05 P.M.	−10.6
12:35 P.M.	−9.4
12:40 P.M.	10
2:20 P.M.	14.4
2:25 P.M.	−8.3

Create a graph of the temperature changes.

1. **Which quadrants do you need for your graph? Explain your reasoning.**

2. **Draw and label the axes for the graph. Then graph the data and connect consecutive points.**

3. **Between which two times was the temperature swing the greatest?**

4. **Describe the pattern. Why is this called an "interesting" day?**

ACTIVITY
3.3   No Place Like Home

Suppose this graph summarizes your day. The x-axis of this graph represents time in minutes from 12:00 P.M., and the y-axis represents your distance from home in blocks. Locations north of your house are positive, and locations south of your house are negative. A point at the origin represents you being home at 12:00 P.M.

Graph A

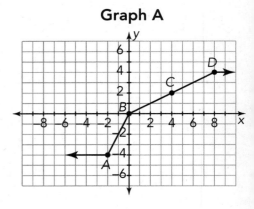

1. Describe the meaning of each of the four labeled points.

x	y	Meaning
−2	−4	
0	0	
4	2	
8	4	

2. Adrian and Sierra are discussing how the graph should look before x = −6 and after x = 10. Adrian thinks he should draw arrows to indicate that the graph continues to the left and right, respectively. Sierra disagrees and thinks they should draw segments back to the x-axis. Who is correct?

Let's consider another graph.

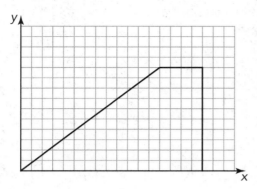

3. Write a possible scenario for this graph. Be sure to specify the units and the meaning of the origin for your scenario.

_____

_____

_____

_____

Natasha and her family took a 3-day trip to her grandmother's house. On the first day, they drove 300 miles. On the second day, they drove 350 miles. On the third day, they drove the remaining 200 miles.

4. Create a graph to represent Natasha's family trip. Be sure to label your axes with quantities and units and label specific points that highlight the trip.

Nadja is coordinating the neighborhood Spring Fling. She asks Matthew to blow up balloons for the event. The graphs shown represent his efforts.

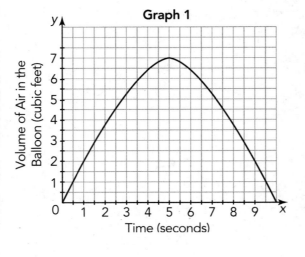

Graph 1

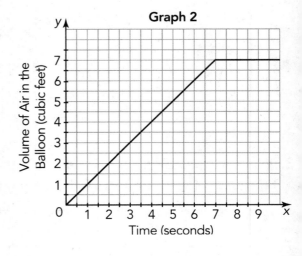

Graph 2

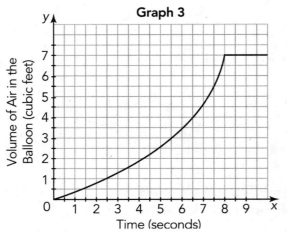

Graph 3

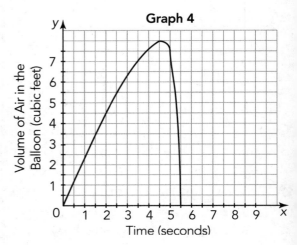

Graph 4

5. Analyze each graph shown, and then answer each question.

    a. What quantity is represented on the x-axis in each graph?

    b. What quantity is represented on the y-axis in each graph?

    c. Which quantity is independent quantity and which is dependent quantity?

6. Match each description with the appropriate graph.

    a. Matthew blows air into a balloon at a steady rate, then ties
        it off when it is full.

    b. Matthew blows air into a balloon, and then the
        balloon pops!

    c. Matthew blows air into a balloon, and then lets the air out.

    d. Matthew blows air into a balloon slowly. As the balloon
        stretches out, he is able to blow more air into the balloon.
        He then ties off the balloon when it is full.

ACTIVITY
3.4 | **Pool Level**

The graph shows the water level of a pool. The x-axis represents time, in hours, and the y-axis represents the water level, in inches. The origin represents 3:00 P.M. and the desired water level.

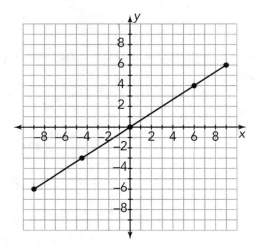

1. **Label the graph with the independent and dependent quantities and their units.**

2. **Create a table of values for the points plotted and describe the meaning of each.**

x	y	Meaning

3. At what rate did the water go into the pool? Explain your reasoning.

4. Describe a situation that would match the graph.

5. Write an equation for this situation.

6. Why does the graph stop rather than continue infinitely?

7. Using any of your mathematical tools, determine the time when the pool was 3 inches above the desired fill level. Is your answer exact or approximate? Explain.

ACTIVITY
3.5 Water in the Bucket

As part of a science project, Damon collected water in a bucket in his backyard and is studying the evaporation. Unfortunately, Damon is a bit forgetful and forgets to take measurements of the water every day. The first day he remembered was Sunday, which was 4 days AFTER the data collection was to begin. He collects the following data.

Days Since Sunday	Height of Water (inches)
0	27
5	22
7	20
12	15

1. Graph the data. Connect the data values with a line. Be sure to label your axes.

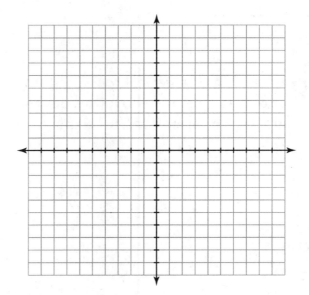

3. Define variables for the hours worked and Aidan's pay.

4. Write an equation to describe Aidan's graph.

5. Use the tool of your choice—equation, graph, or a table—to answer each equation.

   a. Approximately how much money did Aidan make if he worked 15 hours this week?

   b. Determine the exact amount of money Aidan made if he worked 12 hours this week.

   c. Approximately how many hours did Aidan work if he made $50 this week?

   d. Determine the exact number of hours Aidan worked if he made $152.50 this week.

   e. How did you decide which tool to use to answer each question?

ACTIVITY
3.7

Broken Yardstick

Jason and Liliana need to measure some pictures so they can buy picture frames. They looked for something to use to measure the pictures, but could find only a broken yardstick. The yardstick was missing the first $2\frac{1}{2}$ inches.

They both thought about how to use this yardstick.

Lilianna said that all they had to do was measure the pictures and then subtract $2\frac{1}{2}$ inches from each measurement.

1. Is Lilianna correct? Explain your reasoning.

2. They measured the first picture's length and width to be 11 inches and $9\frac{1}{2}$ inches. What are the actual length and width?

3. Define variables for a measurement with the broken yardstick and the actual measurement.

4. Write an equation that models the relationship between the variables.

5. Complete the table of values for the measurement on the yardstick and the actual measurement.

Measurement with Broken Yardstick (in.)	Actual Measurement (in.)
11	8
$9\frac{1}{2}$	$6\frac{1}{2}$
$25\frac{3}{4}$	$22\frac{3}{4}$
21	18
$18\frac{5}{8}$	$15\frac{5}{8}$
15	12
$32\frac{1}{8}$	$29\frac{1}{8}$
$9\frac{7}{8}$	$6\frac{7}{8}$

6. Use the table to complete the graph of the actual measurements versus the measurement taken with the broken yardstick.

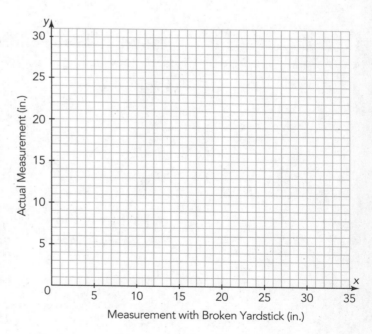

Actual Measurement (in.)

Measurement with Broken Yardstick (in.)

7. Would it make sense to connect the points on this graph? Explain why or why not.

8. Suppose the yardstick was broken at 5 inches instead of $2\frac{1}{2}$ inches.

a. Write the new equation for the relationship between the actual measurement and the measurement from the broken yardstick.

b. Sketch a graph of the actual measurements versus the measurement taken with the new broken yardstick on the graph with the original yardstick.

c. What do you notice about the two graphs?

d. What is the meaning of the x-intercept—the point with a y-coordinate of zero—on each graph?

A freediver is a person who dives into the ocean without the use of any breathing device like scuba equipment. William Trubridge holds the record for freediving. In 2016, he broke his own record and dove almost 407 feet into the ocean! Suppose you plan to train as a freediver and want to beat Trubridge's record.

1. **What are some questions you would ask of Trubridge about his dive?**

> Consider which representations would be useful—tables, graphs, or equations.

2. **Assume that Trubridge ascended and descended at the same rate of 2.97 feet per second to help you determine how much time you need to be able to hold your breath to beat Trubridge's record.**

TALK the TALK

Your Turn!

You and your group should prepare a presentation for this problem.

1. **Create a situation that can be modeled by the graph.**

   Write at least 3 sentences for what you want to say during your presentation.

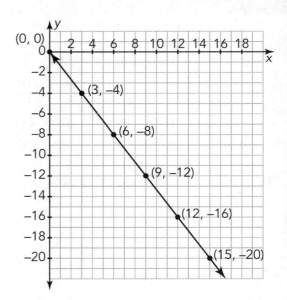

- Be sure to determine the ratio, or rate, for how the variables change in relation to each other.

- Describe the meaning of each point on the graph.

- Define variables for the independent and dependent quantities based on your situation.

- Write an equation to represent the problem situation.

_____

_____

_____

_____

_____

_____

_____

_____

_____

_____

Assignment

Write

Give an example of when you might want to use an equation to answer a question and another example of when you might want to use a graph.

Remember

Graphs, tables, equations, and scenarios provide different information and allow for various levels of accuracy when solving problems.

Practice

1. The gravitational pull of the Moon is not as great as that of Earth. In fact, if a person checks his weight on the Moon, it will be only $\frac{1}{6}$ of his weight on Earth.

   a. If a person weighs 186 pounds on Earth, how much will he weigh on the Moon? How many pounds different from his actual weight is that?

   b. Complete the table of values for a person's weight on Earth, weight on the Moon, and difference of the two weights. Use negative numbers when the weight is less than the person's earth weight.

Weight on Earth (lb)	186	168		198		
Weight on Moon (lb)			29		21	24
Weight Differential	−155					

   c. Graph the weight differential versus the weight on Earth. Be sure to label your axes.

2. To keep her students relaxed and focused during tests, Ms. Chappell puts small bowls of candy on each of their desks. Write a short story to describe each graph.

   a.

   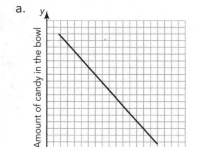

   b.

   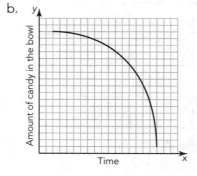

   c.

   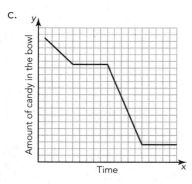

   d.

   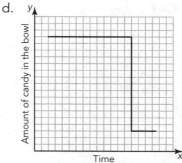

3. The following graph shows the average temperature, in degrees Celsius, in Fairbanks, Alaska. The x-axis represents time in days from January 1, and the y-axis represents degrees Celsius.

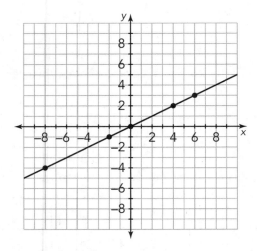

a. Label the axes with the independent and dependent quantities and their units.

b. Create a table of values for the points on the graph and describe the meaning of each.

x	y	Meaning

c. At what rate did the temperature increase?

d. Define variables for the quantities that are changing, and write an equation for this situation.

4. Sarina's dog, Bruno, has to go on a diet! Sarina puts Bruno on a diet plan of daily exercise and a special type of dog food. She estimates Bruno will lose $1\frac{1}{2}$ pounds per week on this plan.

a. How many pounds does Sarina estimate Bruno will lose in 2 weeks? In $8\frac{1}{2}$ weeks?

b. Define variables for the independent and dependent quantities for this situation.

c. Write an equation for this situation. (Because Bruno is losing weight, the number of pounds he loses will be defined as a negative value.)

d. Create a table of values for the situation.

e. Complete a graph of the situation.

f. Explain what points in Quadrant I would mean for Bruno.

Stretch

Tell a story to describe the graph.

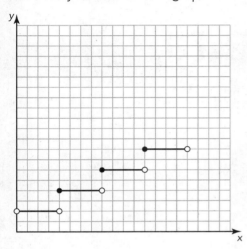

Review

1. The vertices of a polygon are given. Plot the points on a coordinate plane and connect the points in the order they are listed. Then determine the area of the polygon.

   (−4, −1), (−3, −2), (10, −2), (3, 0), (0, 4), (−2, 3)

2. Create a scenario to fit each numeric expression.

   a. |−3 + 21|
   b. |8 − 3|

3. Evaluate each expression for the given values.

   a. 5.2r + 1.2, when r = 1.5 and 4.1
   b. $\frac{1}{2}t + \frac{3}{4}$, when $t = \frac{2}{3}$ and $\frac{9}{5}$

The Four Quadrants Summary

KEY TERM

- quadrants

Four Is Better Than One

The Cartesian coordinate plane is formed by two perpendicular number lines that intersect at the zeros, or the origin. The intersecting number lines divide the plane into four regions, called **quadrants**.

The quadrants are numbered with Roman numerals from one to four (I, II, III, IV) starting in the upper right-hand quadrant and moving counterclockwise.

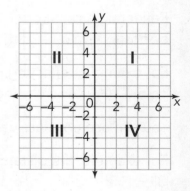

To plot an ordered pair on the coordinate plane, begin at the origin (0, 0), and first move the distance along the x-axis given by the x-value of the ordered pair. Move right for a positive value and move left for a negative value. Then, move the distance along the y-axis given by the y-value of the ordered pair. Move up for a positive value and move down for a negative value.

For example, the following points are plotted on the coordinate plane:

A (−4, 1)
B (−1, 0)
C (−6, −5)
D (2, −3)
E (0, 3)
F (5, 3)

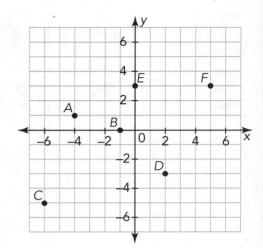

The values of the coordinates of points that are in the same quadrant will be have the same sign before their x- and y-values.

Quadrant II	Quadrant I
(−x, +y)	(+x, +y)
Quadrant III	**Quadrant IV**
(−x, −y)	(+x, −y)

Reflecting a point on the coordinate plane across the x-axis results in a new point with the same x-value and the opposite y-value as the original point.

For example, reflecting point A (8, 4) across the x-axis gives point A' (8, −4). Reflecting point B (−5, −9) across the x-axis gives point B' (−5, 9).

Reflecting a point on the coordinate plane across the y-axis results in a new point with the opposite x-value and the same y-value as the original point.

For example, reflecting point C (3, −2) across the y-axis gives point A' (−3, −2). Reflecting point D (−1, 0) across the y-axis gives point B' (1, 0).

You can use absolute value to determine distances on the coordinate plane.

For example, the distance from point P to point Q is |3| + |−3| = 3 + 3 = 6 units.

The distance from point P to point S is |−6| + |6| = 6 + 6 = 12 units.

The distance from point R to point S is |6| − |3| = 6 − 3 = 3 units.

The distance from point Q to point T is |−7| − |−3| = 7 − 3 = 4 units.

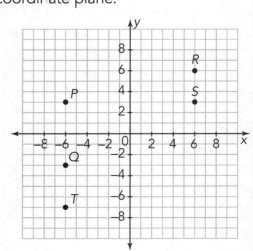

It's a Bird, It's a Plane...It's a Polygon on the Plane!

One advantage of the Cartesian coordinate plane is that it enables mathematicians to use coordinates to analyze geometric figures.

For example, the points in the table have been graphed on the coordinate plane and connected to form a polygon.

x	y
1	1
5	1
5	−4
1	−4

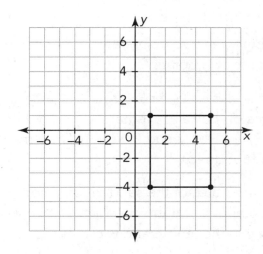

The polygon has opposite sides that are parallel and congruent, so it is a parallelogram. It also has four right angles, so it is a rectangle. The perimeter and area of the rectangle can be calculated by first determining its length and width. The length of the rectangle is 5 units and the width of the rectangle is 4 units.

Perimeter: 4 + 5 + 4 + 5 = 18 units   Area: 5 × 4 = 20 square units

There is often more than one way to complete a polygon on the coordinate plane when given a segment.

For example, on the coordinate plane, the line segment *AB* is graphed.

Plot and label points *C* and *D* to form a parallelogram with a height of 6 units.

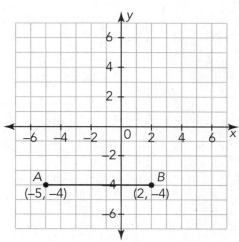

Two different examples of Parallelogram ABCD are shown. Each has a length of 7 units and height of 6 units, so they both have an area of 7 × 6 = 42 square units.

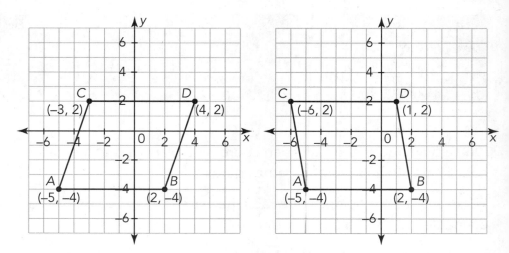

The distance between two points on a coordinate plane can be calculated by using the coordinates of the two points.

For example, the design of a playground is laid out in a grid with a unit of 1 foot. The coordinates of the sand pit that will go under the swing set are located at (−15, 7), (−10, 7), (−15, −1), and (−10, −1). Determine the volume of the sand pit if the pit is 0.5 foot deep.

Plotting the coordinates of the sand pit on a coordinate plane shows that the shape of the sand pit is a rectangle. Use the coordinates to determine the distance between the points which will give you the length and width of the rectangle.

Width: $|{-15}| - |{-10}| = 15 - 10 = 5$ feet
Length: $|7| + |{-1}| = 7 + 1 = 8$ feet

Area: 8 × 5 = 40 square feet
Volume: 8 × 5 × 0.5 = 20 cubic feet

There Are Many Paths...

Graphs, tables, equations, and scenarios provide various information and allow for different levels of accuracy when solving problems.

For example, the graph given shows the water level of a pool. The x-axis represents time, in hours, and the y-axis represents the water level, in inches.

The origin represents 3:00 P.M. and the desired water level.

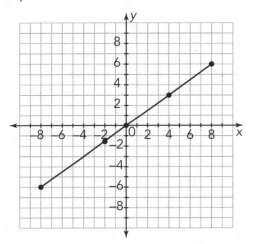

You can create a table of values for the points plotted and describe the meaning of each.

x	y	Meaning
−8	−6	At 7:00 A.M., the water level is 6 inches below the desired water level.
−2	$-1\frac{1}{2}$	At 1:00 P.M., the water level is $1\frac{1}{2}$ inches below the desired water level.
0	0	At 3:00 P.M., the water is at the desired water level.
4	3	At 7:00 P.M., the water level is 4 inches above the desired water level.
8	6	At 11:00 P.M., the water level is 6 inches above the desired water level.

You can use the graph to determine that the water went into the pool at a rate of $\frac{3}{4}$ inch per hour. An equation that represents this situation would by $y = \frac{3}{4}x$.

MODULE 5

DESCRIBING VARIABILITY OF QUANTITIES

The lessons in this module build on the data displays that you have used in elementary school, namely line plots, bar graphs, and circle graphs. You will be introduced to the field of statistics, the study of data, and the statistical problem-solving process. You will calculate numerical summaries to describe a data set. You will also learn what separates mathematical and statistical reasoning—the presence of variability.

The Statistical Process

On average, one out of every 25 sheep has black wool. A quick way to estimate the size of a flock of sheep is to count the black sheep and multiply by 25.

Module 5: Describing Variability of Quantities

TOPIC 1: THE STATISTICAL PROCESS

In this topic, students are introduced to the statistical problem-solving process: formulate questions, collect data, analyze data, and interpret the results. Students will use this process throughout their studies of statistics, increasing the complexity of each step of the process as they develop their statistical literacy. Students use bar graphs and pie charts to analyze and interpret survey data, the final steps of the statistical process. As students learn about and analyze dot plots, stem-and-leaf plots, and histograms, they practice using the four steps of the statistical process.

Where have we been?

In grade 1, students were expected to organize, represent, and interpret data with up to three categories. In grades 2 and 3, students created picture graphs and bar graphs of categorical data. In grades 4 and 5, students made line plots to display data with fractions. And in grade 4, students developed a conceptual understanding of angles and angle measurement, allowing them to create pie charts.

Where are we going?

In grade 7, students will use the data displays learned in this topic to compare data distributions. They will use statistical problem solving to investigate and draw inferences about populations. In grade 8, students will move into comparing two variables with data.

Histograms

A histogram is a graphical way to display quantitative or numerical data using vertical bars. The width of a bar in a histogram represents an interval of data and is often referred to as a bin. The height of the bar indicates the frequency, or the number of data values included in any given bin. Bins are represented by intervals of data instead of showing individual data values.

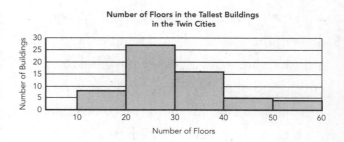

Number of Floors in the Tallest Buildings in the Twin Cities

Myth: Faster = smarter.

In most cases, speed has nothing to do with how smart you are. Why is that? Because it largely depends on how familiar you are with a topic. For example, a bike mechanic can look at a bike for about 8 seconds and tell you details about the bike that you probably didn't even notice (e.g., the front tire is on backwards). Is that person smart? Sure! Suppose, instead, you show the same bike mechanic a car. Will they be able to report the same amount of detail as they did for the bike? No!

It's easy to confuse *speed* with *understanding*. Speed is associated with the memorization of facts. Understanding, on the other hand, is a methodical, time-consuming process. Understanding is the result of asking lots of questions and seeing connections between different ideas. Many mathematicians who won the Fields Medal (i.e., the Nobel prize for mathematics) describe themselves as extremely slow thinkers. That's because mathematical thinking requires understanding over memorization.

#mathmythbusted

Talking Points

You can support your student's learning by approaching problems slowly. Students may observe a classmate learning things very quickly, and they can easily come to believe that mathematics is about getting the right answer as quickly as possible. When this doesn't happen for them, future encounters with math can raise anxiety, making problem solving more difficult, and reinforcing a student's view of himself or herself as "not good at math." Slowing down is not the ultimate cure for math difficulties. But it's a good first step for children who are struggling. You can reinforce the view that learning with understanding takes time, and that slow, deliberate work is the rule, not the exception.

Key Terms

categorical data
Categorical data are data for which each piece of data fits into exactly one of several different groups or categories. Categorical data are also called *qualitative data*.

quantitative data
Quantitative data are data for which each piece of data can be placed on a numerical scale. Quantitative data are also called *numerical data*.

frequency
Frequency is the number of times an item or number occurs in a data set.

mode
The mode is the value or values that occur most frequently in a data set.

What's Your Question?

Understanding the Statistical Process

WARM UP

Ms. White asked the 25 sixth graders in her class, "How many pets do typical 6th graders in our class have?" Ms. White summarized the responses in the table.

Number of Students	Number of Pets
8	0
10	1
4	2
2	3
1	38

1. About how many pets does each sixth grader in Ms. White's class own? How did you make your decision?

LEARNING GOALS

- Recognize and design statistical questions and anticipate variability in data related to the question.
- Differentiate between surveys, observational studies, and experiments.
- Describe the four stages of the statistical process.
- Discuss the different types of data that can be collected, displayed, and analyzed.
- Analyze and interpret bar graphs and circle graphs.

KEY TERMS

- variability
- data
- statistical question
- statistical process
- categorical data
- quantitative data
- population
- sample
- survey
- observational study
- experiment
- bar graph
- circle graph
- frequency
- mode

You have been solving mathematical problems throughout this course. Now, you are going to study statistical problems. How are mathematics and statistics similar and different?

In statistics, **variability** means that the value of the attribute being studied can change from one person or thing to another.

Data are categories, numbers, or observations gathered in response to a statistical question.

Statistical or Not, That Is the Question

Have you ever wondered, "How much money do professional athletes make?" Or, "How long are the books assigned to sixth graders?" If so, you have asked a statistical question. If you have sought out the answer to your question, you have engaged in the statistical process.

Cut out the questions provided at the end of the lesson. Read each question and sort them into as many groups as you would like. There must be more than one group and there must be at least two questions per group.

1. **Record your groups and the questions in each group.**

In this module, you will begin your formal study of statistics and the statistical process. Statistics is a problem-solving process, also called an investigative process, because the heart of statistics is about determining a possible answer to a question that has *variability*.

Statistical problem solving begins with a *statistical question*. A **statistical question** is a question that anticipates an answer based on *data* that vary.

2. **Which questions from your sort are statistical questions? Explain how you would expect the answers to those questions to vary.**

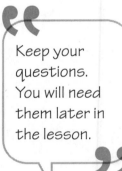

Keep your questions. You will *need* them later in the lesson.

ACTIVITY 1.1 Formulating Statistical Questions

The **statistical process** has four components:

- Formulating a statistical question.
- Collecting appropriate data.
- Analyzing the data graphically and numerically.
- Interpreting the results of the analysis.

This lesson provides an overview of the statistical process, but you will continue to use the process throughout your study of statistics. Statistics is about posing interesting questions that you want to answer about varying attributes.

Analyze the questions posed by Bianca and Rajan.

Bianca

"What clubs am I in?"
"How many students are in the Chess Club?"

Rajan

"What clubs do my classmates belong to?"
"How many members do the clubs at my school have?"

1. **Explain why Bianca's questions are not statistical questions but Rajan's are.**

2. **What kinds of answers do you expect from Rajan's questions?**

Categorical data, or *qualitative data*, are data for which each piece of data fits into exactly one of several different groups or categories.

Quantitative data, or *numerical data*, are data for which each piece of data can be placed on a numerical scale and compared.

> " Just as graphs can be described as discrete or continuous, quantitative data can be described as discrete or continuous. "

Answering a statistical question requires collecting variable data. You will learn about two types of data: *categorical data* and *quantitative data*.

3. Would the answers to Rajan's questions be categorical or quantitative?

4. Gather the statistical questions from the *Statistical or Not* activity. Which questions have categorical answers and which have quantitative answers?

5. For each question, determine if it is a statistical question. If it is not, rewrite it as a statistical question. Then, state if the data would be categorical or quantitative.

   a. How many text messages did you send and receive yesterday?

   b. What are the most popular school mascots?

   c. How much time did you spend watching TV or playing video games last weekend?

d. How many hours do 6th graders sleep each night?

Some data, like area codes, are numbers but are not quantitative variables. This data serves as a label, or category.

e. What is your favorite sport?

6. Write at least 2 additional statistical questions that you would be interested in answering. State if the data would be categorical or quantitative.

Don't worry about the answer to the question, if there even is one. What would you like to know?

For this activity, let's consider the topic of school lunches.

1. **Write three statistical questions that you can ask about school lunches.**

   a.

   b.

   c.

The second component of the statistical process is to collect the data to answer the statistical question.

A statistical question can be answered by collecting data from an entire *population* or, more commonly, from a *sample* of the population. A **population** is an entire set of items from which data are collected. A **sample** is a selection from a population.

For example, to answer the question "How tall are 6th graders?" using the population of all 6th graders, you would need to determine the heights of every 6th grader in the world. However, you could choose to answer the question by collecting data from a sample of 6th graders—the 6th graders at your school.

Three common methods of data collection are *surveys*, *observational studies*, and *experiments*. In a **survey**, people are asked one or more questions. Similarly, in an **observational study**, the researcher (you!) collects data by observing the variable of interest. In an **experiment**, the researcher imposes a condition and observes the results.

You could conduct an experiment to investigate if 6th graders perform better on an assessment if they read a textbook or watch a video about the material. You would randomly assign half the students to read the text and half the students to watch the video. All students would be given the same assessment. You would compare the scores of the students in the two groups.

2. **For each statistical question you wrote in Question 1, identify the population and sample of interest.**

   a.

   b.

   c.

If you have ever completed a science project, you have probably conducted an experiment.

3. **Do you think a survey, observational study, or experiment would be the best way to collect the data to answer your statistical questions? Explain your reasoning.**

   a.

   b.

   c.

ACTIVITY 1.3

Analyzing and Interpreting Data

Formulating a statistical question is Part 1 of the statistical process.

Suppose you are interested in characteristics of sixth graders at your school.

1. **Formulate three categorical statistical questions and survey your class to obtain a sample.**

Collecting data is Part 2 of the statistical process.

Analyzing the collected data is Part 3 of the statistical process.

In the statistical process, after you collect the data, it is time to analyze and interpret the results. Analysis includes selecting the most appropriate graphical display and numerical summaries for your question and your method of data collection.

You already have experience displaying and summarizing categorical data using *bar graphs* and *circle graphs*.

A **bar graph** displays categorical data using either horizontal or vertical bars on a graph. The height or length of each bar indicates the value for that category.

A **circle graph**, often called a pie chart, displays categorical data using sectors, or "wedges," of a circle. It shows how parts of the whole relate to the whole and how parts of the whole relate to the other parts. The area of each sector corresponds to the percentage of the part in relation to the whole.

Nicole and Neal were interested in the favorite sports of 6th graders. They surveyed their class of 30 students. Then, they displayed their class's data in different ways. Analyze each graph.

Nicole

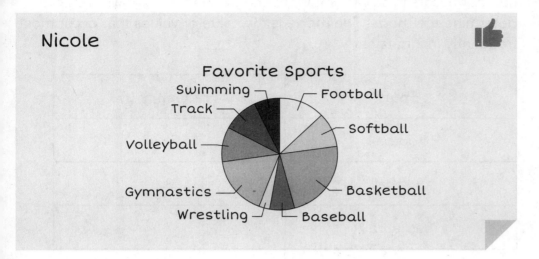

Neal

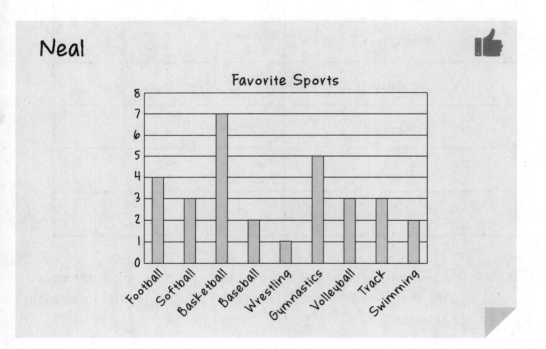

2. How are the graphs similar? How are they different?

In order to create the graphs, Nicole and Neal determined the *frequency* of each response and recorded the frequencies in a frequency table. A **frequency** is the number of times an item or number occurs in a data set. Once the frequency is known, you can determine the *mode*. The **mode** is the value or values that occur most frequently in a data set.

Sport	Frequency (f)
Football	4
Softball	3
Basketball	7
Baseball	2
Wrestling	1
Gymnastics	5
Volleyball	3
Track	3
Swimming	2

Interpreting the data, or drawing conclusions, is Part 4 of the statistical process.

3. **What conclusions can you make about the most popular sport in Nicole and Neal's class? Use the table and graphs to explain your reasoning.**

4. Compile your class's responses to the 3 survey questions you asked in Question 1. Record the frequency of each response in a table.

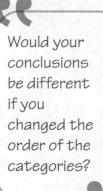

Would your conclusions be different if you changed the order of the categories?

5. Create a graphical display for your assigned survey question. What conclusions can you make about your class based on your graph?

TALK the TALK 💬

(Graphically) Organizing the Process

Complete the graphic organizer for the statistical process. In each section, summarize what you know about the component and provide examples.

1. Formulate a Statistical Question

2. Collect Data

STATISTICAL PROCESS

3. Analyze the Data

4. Interpret the Results

A What is your favorite sport?	**B** How many TVs are in your house?	**C** What is the most popular favorite color in the school?
D How far do I travel to school?	**E** What grade did I earn on my last math test?	**F** How many siblings do I have?
G How many siblings do 6th graders have?	**H** How tall are 6th graders?	**I** How many TVs are in a U.S. household?
J What is your favorite color?	**K** How many clubs are at my school?	**L** How tall am I?
M What kinds of sports do 6th graders prefer?	**N** How far do the students at my school travel to get to school each day?	**O** What grades were earned on the last math test?

Assignment

Write

Match each definition to its corresponding term.

1. an entire set of items from which data can be selected
2. the information that is collected from an experiment, study, or survey
3. a question that anticipates variability
4. imposing a condition to test a specific result
5. a method for collecting information by asking one or more questions
6. a method for collecting information by observing a phenomenon in action
7. a subset of a population
8. the value of an attribute, or quality, being studied can change from one person or thing to another
9. data for which each piece of data fits into exactly one of several different groups or categories
10. data which can be placed on a numerical scale and compared, and can consist of discrete or continuous variables
11. a graph that shows how parts of the whole relate to the whole and how parts relate to other parts
12. a way of displaying categorical data by using either horizontal or vertical bars so that the height or length of the bars indicates the value for that category
13. the number of times an item or number occurs in a data set
14. the observation or value that occurs the most

a. data
b. experiment
c. bar graph
d. variability
e. statistical question
f. categorical data
g. circle graph
h. survey
i. observational study
j. population
k. sample
l. frequency
m. mode
n. quantitative data

Remember

There are four components to the statistical process:
- Formulate a statistical question.
- Collect data.
- Analyze the data using graphical displays and numerical summaries.
- Interpret the results in terms of the original statistical question and context.

Practice

1. Determine whether each given question is a statistical question. If not, rewrite it to make it a statistical question.
   a. How many people in your class like to play video games?
   b. Is pizza your favorite food?
   c. What time do you go to bed on school nights?

2. Determine whether a survey, observational study, or experiment would be the best way to answer each given statistical question.
   a. "How many of the students in your class ate breakfast this morning?"
   b. "Which students in your school can run a 40-meter sprint the fastest?"
   c. "How many students in your class can type at least 30 words per minute?"
   d. "How many students in your class ride the bus to school each day?"

3. Determine whether each set of given data are categorical or quantitative. If the data are quantitative, determine whether they are discrete or continuous.
   a. Each student in your math class records their height.
   b. The members of the Horse Club list the types of horses they have.
   c. The members of the Horse Club list the numbers of horses they each have.

4. Tamara claims that Sweet Grove apple juice tastes better than Juicy Bushels apple juice. Isaac claims that there is no difference between the 2 types of apple juice. Tamara and Isaac would like to find the answer to the following question: Do more 6th graders prefer Sweet Grove apple juice or Juicy Bushels apple juice?
   a. Is this a statistical question? Explain your reasoning.
   b. Explain how this question can be answered with an experiment.

5. The circle graph shows the results of the vote for the new school mascot.
   a. If 400 students voted, how many students voted for the Cheetahs?
   b. Create a bar graph to display the information, in terms of frequency, of each mascot.
   c. What conclusions about the question of what mascot should be adopted can you make based on the graphs?

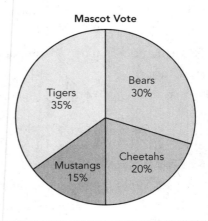

Mascot Vote

Tigers 35%
Bears 30%
Mustangs 15%
Cheetahs 20%

Stretch

In 1945, George Polya published a book about mathematical problem solving. He outlined a four-step process for problem solving:

1. Understand the Problem
2. Devise a Plan
3. Carry out the Plan
4. Look Back

Research the four steps and explain how the four-component statistical problem-solving process is similar to and different from Polya's four steps for mathematical problem solving.

Review

1. Choose the graph that best represents each scenario. Explain your reasoning.

   a. Carla fills a mug with tea. Every few minutes Carla takes a drink from the mug.

   A.  B.  C.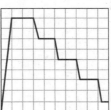

   b. When Jamal rides his bike up a hill, his speed decreased. When he rides down a hill, his speed increased.

   A.  B. 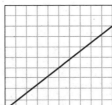 C.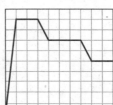

2. Use absolute value equations to justify each answer.

   a. Determine the distance between the horizontal lines that contain points A (7, 5) and B (−4, −8).

   b. Determine the distance between the vertical lines that contain points A (7, 5) and B (−4, −8).

3. Insert a >, <, or = symbol to make each number sentence true.

   a. $-9\frac{1}{8}$ _____ -9.4 b. 0.006 _____ 1%

Get in Shape 2

Analyzing Numerical Data Displays

WARM UP

Mr. Garcia surveyed his class and asked them what types of pets they owned. Analyze the pictograph that shows the results of his survey:

Pets Owned by Students in Mr. Garcia's Class
(each symbol represents 1 student)

Dogs	🐈	🐈	🐈	🐈	🐈	🐈	🐈
Cat	🐱	🐱	🐱	🐱	🐱	🐱	🐱	🐱
Fish	🐟	🐟	🐟	🐟			
Birds	🐦	🐦					
Other	*	*	*	*			

1. How many students in Mr. Garcia's class own dogs?

2. How many students own fish or birds?

3. Can you tell by looking at the pictograph how many students own pets? Why or why not?

LEARNING GOALS
- Create and interpret dot plots.
- Create and interpret stem-and-leaf plots.
- Describe the center, spread, and overall shape of a data distribution.

KEY TERMS
- dot plot
- distribution
- symmetric
- skewed right
- skewed left
- clusters
- gaps
- peaks
- outliers
- stem-and-leaf plot

You know how to use picture graphs, bar graphs, and line plots to display categorical and numerical data. What additional plots can be used to display and analyze numerical data?

Rock-Climbing Competition

Ms. Nicholson poses the question "Which grade has the fastest average rock-climbing time if each student is given one attempt?"

She selects one class from each grade level, times each student as they climb the rock wall, and records the times. Then she creates data displays for each class.

Sixth Grade Completion Times (seconds):

60, 50, 58, 59, 60, 54, 55, 58, 59, 60, 52, 54, 56, 57, 57, 58, 60, 60, 59, 58

Seventh Grade Completion Times (seconds):

51, 52, 53, 53, 54, 54, 54, 55, 55, 55, 55, 55, 56, 56, 56, 56, 57, 57, 58, 60

Eighth Grade Completion Times (seconds):

48, 54, 53, 50, 54, 52, 48, 49, 51, 54, 53, 48, 50, 50, 49, 51, 51, 52, 53

Rock-Climbing Times (6th Grade)

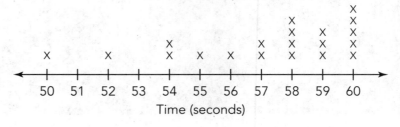

Rock-Climbing Times (7th Grade)

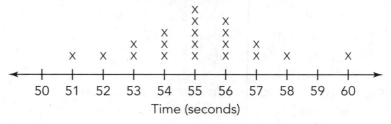

Rock-Climbing Times (8th Grade)

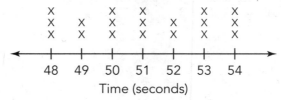

1. **How are these data displays similar? How are they different?**

2. **What can you observe from a data display that you cannot see from looking at the numerical data?**

Creating and Analyzing Dot Plots

The 2014 Winter Olympics were held in Sochi, Russia. While watching the Olympics, Jessica and Maurice decided to pose statistical questions about the Games.

1. Jessica asked, "How many medals did the United States win? How many of those were gold?" Maurice thought a better set of questions would be, "What is the typical number of medals won? What is the typical number of gold medals won by a country?" Who's correct? Explain your reasoning.

The table at the end of the lesson lists the number of gold medals and the total medals won by all medal-winning countries for the 2014 Winter Olympics.

2. Analyze the data shown in the table.

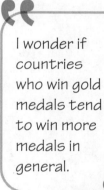

I wonder if countries who win gold medals tend to win more medals in general.

   a. What conclusions can you make about the numbers of total medals won at the 2014 Winter Olympics?

   b. Are the data in the table categorical or quantitative? Explain your reasoning.

   c. Are the data in the table discrete or continuous? Explain your reasoning.

One way to describe a set of quantitative data is by drawing a graphical display of the data.

A **dot plot** is a data display that shows discrete data on a number line with dots, Xs, or other symbols. Dot plots help organize and display a small number of data points.

WORKED EXAMPLE

This dot plot shows the gold-medal data. The number line represents the number of gold medals. Each X above a number represents the number of countries that won that many gold medals.

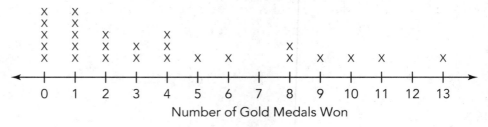

3. Use the dot plot to answer each question.

   a. What do the two Xs above the number 8 represent?

   b. What do the five Xs above the number 0 represent?

   c. Why are there no Xs above the number 7?

   d. Use the dot plot to determine the number of countries that won medals in the 2014 Winter Olympics. Explain your strategy.

Let's create a dot plot to display the total number of medals won as listed in the 2014 Winter Olympics data table.

4. Make a plan for creating your dot plot.

    a. What will you name your dot plot?

    b. What numbers will begin and end your number line? Why did you select these numbers?

    c. What interval will you use on your number line? Why did you select this interval?

5. Create your dot plot displaying the data for the total medals won at the 2014 Winter Olympics.

6. Write a brief summary to report the results of your data analysis back to Maurice and Jessica to help answer their questions about gold medals and all medals won at the 2014 Winter Olympics.

Describing Distributions

> These questions are part of analyzing data.

When you analyze a graphical representation of numeric data, you can look at its shape, center, and spread to draw conclusions.

• What is the overall shape of the graph? Does it have any interesting patterns?

• Where is the approximate middle, or center, of the graph?

• What does the graph tell me about how spread out the data values are?

The overall shape of a graph is called the *distribution* of data. A **distribution** is the way in which the data are spread out.

The shape of the distribution can reveal a lot of information about data. There are many different distributions, but the most common are *symmetric*, *skewed right*, and *skewed left*.

Shapes of Typical Distributions of Graphical Displays of Data

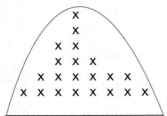

symmetric

- The left and right halves of the graph are mirror images of each other.

- The peak is in the middle, because there are many data values in the center.

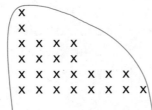

skewed right

- The peak of the data is to the left side of the graph.

- There are only a few data points to the right side of the graph.

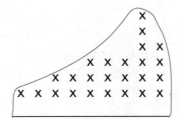

skewed left

- The peak of the data is to the right side of the graph.

- There are only a few data points to the left side of the graph.

A peak is usually the value with the greatest frequency, or one of the values with the greatest frequency, and is often surrounded by data values with other large numbers of data points.

1. **Miko says that the dot plot shown in the previous activity for the number of gold medals won is skewed right. Do you agree with her statement? Explain your reasoning.**

Examine the dot plot you created for the total number of medals won by medal-winning countries.

2. **What is the distribution of the dot plot? Explain what this means in terms of the total number of medals won.**

When analyzing a graphical display of data, you can also look for any interesting patterns. Some of these patterns include:

- **clusters**—areas where data are grouped close together
- **gaps**—areas where there are no data
- **peaks**—values that contain more data points than the values on either side of it
- **outliers**—data values that lie a large distance from the other data. Outliers usually accompany gaps in data.

Examine the dot plot you analyzed for the number of gold medals won by medal-winning countries.

Gaps usually span multiple possible data values.

3. **Identify any clusters, gaps, peaks, or outliers. Explain what this means in terms of the number of gold medals won.**

Examine the dot plot you created for the total number of medals won by medal-winning countries.

4. Identify any clusters, gaps, peaks, or outliers. Explain what this means in terms of the total number of medals won.

Another common shape for a data distribution is a uniform distribution.

Refer back to the dot plots from the *Rock-Climbing Competition* activity at the beginning of the lesson.

5. Describe the shape of each dot plot including its overall shape and any relevant patterns.

Stem-and-Leaf Plots

At the 2014 Winter Olympics, 88 countries competed in the events, but only 26 won medals. By contrast, the 2016 Summer Olympics in Rio de Janeiro, Brazil, had 207 countries compete in the events. Athletes from 80 countries won medals, but only 44 won at least 5 medals.

The table at the end of the lesson lists the total number of medals won by the top-performing countries in the 2016 Summer Olympics.

1. **What comparisons can you make between the number of medals won at the 2014 Winter Olympics and the number of medals won at the 2016 Summer Olympics?**

2. **Do you think using a dot plot would be a good way to organize and analyze the data in the Summer Olympics table? Explain your reasoning.**

A numerical data display that can easily display data sets with a larger range of data values would be helpful to plot the 2016 Summer Olympic data. A **stem-and-leaf plot** is a graphical method used to represent ordered numerical data. Once the data is ordered, the stems and leaves are determined. Typically, the stem is all the digits in a number except the rightmost digit, which is the leaf.

A stem-and-leaf plot displaying the number of medals won in the 2016 Summer Olympics is shown.

3. Use the stem-and-leaf plot to answer each question.

a. Describe what you notice about the stem-and-leaf plot.

**Total Medals Won by Countries
2016 Summer Olympics**

```
 0 | 5 5 5 6 6 6 7 7 7 8 8 8 8 8 9 9
 1 | 0 0 0 1 1 1 1 1 3 3 5 5 7 8 8 8 9 9
 2 | 2 8 9
 3 |
 4 | 1 2 2
 5 | 6
 6 | 7
 7 | 0
 8 |
 9 |
10 |
11 |
12 | 1
```

Key: 4|1 = 41 medals won.

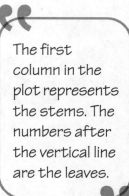

> The first column in the plot represents the stems. The numbers after the vertical line are the leaves.

b. What does 7 | 0 mean in the stem-and-leaf plot?

c. What does 0 | 5 mean?

d. How many stems are in the stem-and-leaf plot?

4. Analyze the stems and leaves in the stem-and-leaf plot.

   a. How many leaves are in the stem-and-leaf plot? Why are there that many leaves?

   b. Why would a stem have more than one leaf?

   c. Why do some stems have no leaves?

   d. Why do some stems have the same leaf repeated?

   e. Carlos claims that he should write 0s as leaves after the stems 3, 8, 9, 10, and 11 to show that there are no countries that have an amount of medals in the 30s, 80s, 90s, 100s, or 110s. Is Carlos correct? Explain your reasoning.

5. What is the most common number of medals won? How can you determine this from the stem-and-leaf plot?

To see the distribution better, rotate the stem-and-leaf plot so that the stems resemble a horizontal number line.

6. Describe the distribution and any interesting patterns you notice in the stem-and-leaf plot. Interpret your findings in terms of the number of medals won in the 2016 Summer Olympics.

ACTIVITY
2.4

Creating and Analyzing Stem-and-Leaf Plots

During the 2016 presidential election, media reports sometimes called attention to the ages of the candidates. This led to Alicia wondering, "Are these candidates too old to be president?" Because she wanted to collect and analyze data, she revised her question: "At what age do presidents take office?"

1. **Explain why Alicia's question is a statistical question.**

To answer her question, Alicia collected data on the ages when the 43 former presidents of the United States were first inaugurated. Her data is presented in the table at the end of the lesson.

To analyze the data, let's create a stem-and-leaf plot of the former presidents' ages at inauguration.

2. **Make a plan for creating the stem-and-leaf plot.**

   a. **What will you choose for your stems? Why did you choose those numbers?**

   b. **How many leaves will you have in your stem-and-leaf plot? Explain your reasoning.**

   c. **Create a key for your stem-and-leaf plot. Why is this needed?**

> Put the data in ascending order, from least to greatest, before filling in the leaves.

3. Create a stem-and-leaf plot to display the age at which each president was inaugurated.

4. Describe the distribution of the ages of presidents at their inaugurations.

5. The minimum age to become president of the United States is 35 years old. How is this requirement reflected in your stem-and-leaf plot?

6. What was the most common age for presidents to be inaugurated? Explain using your stem-and-leaf plot.

The four primary candidates leading into the 2016 presidential election and their projected ages at inauguration are provided.

7. How would your stem-and-leaf plot change if each person had been elected?

Gary Johnson	64
Jill Stein	66
Hillary Clinton	69
Donald Trump	70

8. Write a brief summary to report the results of your data analysis back to Alicia in response to her question about the ages of presidents at their inaugurations.

_____

_____

_____

_____

_____

_____

_____

_____

_____

_____

_____

TALK the TALK

Peaks, Gaps, and Clusters... Oh, My!

Consider the six data displays shown.

Plot A

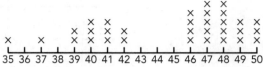

35 36 37 38 39 40 41 42 43 44 45 46 47 48 49 50

Plot B

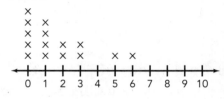

0 1 2 3 4 5 6 7 8 9 10

Plot C

```
1 | 9
2 | 5 5 9
3 | 0 2 2 2 2 4 4 5 6 6 6 9 9 9
4 | 0 0 1 1 2 4 5 6 6 7 7 8 9
5 | 1 1 1 2 3 4 4 6 7
6 | 9
```
5|6 means 56

Plot D

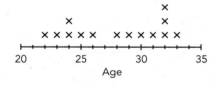

20   25   30   35
                   Age

Plot E

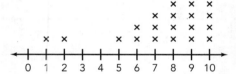

0 1 2 3 4 5 6 7 8 9 10

Plot F

3	2
4	
5	
6	1 4 4
7	2 5 7 9
8	0 2 2 5 6 8
9	0 0 1 2 3 3 5

Key: 3|2 = 3.2

1. **Which plot or plots illustrate each graphical feature?**

   a. **cluster(s)**   b. **gap(s)**   c. **outlier(s)**   d. **skewness**

2. **Select a symmetric distribution and explain how you can make it skewed left or skewed right.**

Use with Activity 2.1, Creating and Analyzing Dot Plots

2014 Winter Olympics All Countries with Medal Wins					
County	Gold Medals	Total Medals	Country	Gold Medals	Total Medals
Russian Federation	13	33	Slovenia	2	8
United States	9	28	Japan	1	8
Norway	11	26	Italy	0	8
Canada	10	25	Belarus	5	6
Netherlands	8	24	Poland	4	6
Germany	8	19	Finland	1	5
Austria	4	17	Great Britain	1	4
France	4	15	Latvia	0	4
Sweden	2	15	Australia	0	3
Switzerland	6	11	Ukraine	1	4
China	3	9	Slovakia	1	1
South Korea	3	8	Croatia	0	1
Czech Republic	2	8	Kazakhstan	0	1

Total Number of Medals Won by Top-Performing Countries, 2016 Summer Olympics			
Country	**Medals Won**	**Country**	**Medals Won**
United States	121	Ukraine	11
China	70	Poland	11
Great Britain	67	Sweden	11
Russian Federation	56	Croatia	10
Germany	42	Czech Republic	10
France	42	South Africa	10
Japan	41	Cuba	9
Australia	29	Belarus	9
Italy	28	Columbia	8
Canada	22	Iran	8
Netherlands	19	Ethiopia	8
Brazil	19	Serbia	8
South Korea	18	Turkey	8
New Zealand	18	Georgia	7
Azerbaijan	18	North Korea	7
Kazakhstan	17	Switzerland	7
Hungary	15	Belgium	6
Denmark	15	Thailand	6
Kenya	13	Greece	6
Uzbekistan	13	Romania	5
Spain	11	Malaysia	5
Jamaica	11	Mexico	5

President	Age at First Inauguration	President	Age at First Inauguration
Washington	57	Harrison	55
Adams, J.	61	McKinley	54
Jefferson	57	Roosevelt, T.	42
Madison	57	Taft	51
Monroe	58	Wilson	56
Adams, J.Q.	57	Harding	55
Jackson	61	Coolidge	51
Van Buren	54	Hoover	54
Harrison	68	Roosevelt, F.D.	51
Tyler	51	Truman	60
Polk	49	Eisenhower	62
Taylor	64	Kennedy	43
Fillmore	50	Johnson, L.B.	55
Pierce	48	Nixon	56
Buchanan	65	Ford	61
Lincoln	52	Carter	52
Johnson, A.	56	Reagan	69
Grant	46	Bush, G.H.W.	64
Hayes	54	Clinton	46
Garfield	49	Bush, G.W.	54
Arthur	50	Obama	47
Cleveland	47		

Use with the Assignment.

Season	Wins	Losses	Season	Wins	Losses
2015-2016	48	34	1991-1992	38	44
2014-2015	60	22	1990-1991	43	39
2013-2014	38	44	1989-1990	41	41
2012-2013	44	38	1988-1989	52	30
2011-2012	40	26	1987-1988	50	32
2010-2011	44	38	1986-1987	57	25
2009-2010	53	29	1985-1986	50	32
2008-2009	47	35	1984-1985	34	48
2007-2008	37	45	1983-1984	40	42
2006-2007	30	52	1982-1983	43	39
2005-2006	26	56	1981-1982	42	40
2004-2005	13	69	1980-1981	31	51
2003-2004	28	54	1979-1980	50	32
2002-2003	35	47	1978-1979	46	36
2001-2002	33	49	1977-1978	41	41
2000-2001	25	57	1976-1977	31	51
1999-2000	28	54	1975-1976	29	53
1998-1999	31	19	1974-1975	31	51
1997-1998	50	32	1973-1974	35	47
1996-1997	56	26	1972-1973	46	36
1995-1996	46	36	1971-1972	36	46
1994-1995	42	40	1970-1971	36	46
1993-1994	57	25	1969-1970	48	34
1992-1993	43	39	1968-1969	48	34

Assignment

Write

Write a definition for each of term in your own words.

1. dot plot
2. distribution
3. symmetric
4. skewed right
5. skewed left
6. clusters
7. gaps
8. peaks
9. outliers
10. stem-and-leaf plot

Remember

Data sets have distributions that can be described according to their shape.
Dot plots are ideal for small data sets.
Stem-and-leaf plots are ideal for moderately sized data sets, especially if you need to see the actual data values.

Practice

The data table at the end of the lesson shows the number of wins and losses the Atlanta Hawks have had in 48 seasons in Atlanta.

1. Create a dot plot or a stem-and-leaf plot for the number of wins by the Atlanta Hawks. Be sure to name your plot and provide a key if necessary.
2. Describe the distribution of the data. Include any specific graphical features or patterns. Explain what your answer means in terms of the number of wins by the Hawks.
3. Create a dot plot or a stem-and-leaf plot for the number of losses by the Atlanta Hawks. Be sure to name your plot and provide a key if necessary.
4. Describe the distribution of the data. Include any specific graphical features or patterns. Explain what your answer means in terms of the number of losses by the Hawks.
5. Propose a win-loss record for an upcoming season that would result in a change in the overall distribution of both plots.

Stretch

Another type of display used to compare two data sets is a side-by-side or back-to-back stem-and-leaf plot.

1. Describe the distribution of each data set.
2. Then, use the key and the plot to list the numerical data values in each data set.

Data Set One			Data Set Two
8 6	4		
9 3 1	5	9	
9 8 6 5 1 1	0	6	2 7
7 3 2	7	0 0 3 6 6 8 9	
5 3	8	0 1 1 2	
2 1	9		

Key: 1|5|9 = 5.1 and 5.9

Review

1. Write a statistical question about each situation.
   a. vacation destinations
   b. books

2. Plot and identify 4 points on a coordinate plane that are vertices of a parallelogram. Include points in more than one quadrant. Draw the parallelogram. Write absolute value statements for the length of the base and height of your parallelogram. Then, determine the area of the parallelogram.

3. Use long division to determine each quotient.
   a. 247 ÷ 8
   b. 894 ÷ 12

Skyscrapers **3**

Using Histograms to Display Data

WARM UP

Use the bar graph to answer each question.

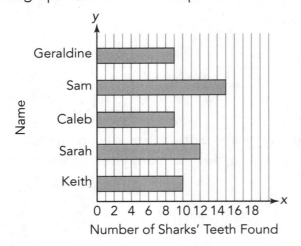

1. Who found the most sharks' teeth? How many did that person find?

2. How many total sharks' teeth did the friends find?

LEARNING GOALS

- Display and interpret numerical data in histograms.
- Compare data displays.

KEY TERMS

- histogram
- grouped frequency table

You have used dot plots and stem-and-leaf plots, which are good for small data sets. How can you display data sets with a larger number of observations?

State Parks

There are over 6000 state parks in the United States. The table shows how many state parks there are in each of the states listed.

State	Number of Parks
Colorado	42
Arizona	30
Nevada	24
Georgia	66
Tennessee	56
Alabama	27
Vermont	57
New Hampshire	75
Rhode Island	23

1. Create a bar graph using the data in the table.

2. Create another bar graph with the states in alphabetical order. How is this bar graph different from your previous bar graph?

The remainder of this lesson is about *histograms*, which look similar to bar graphs.

3. Suppose you wanted to graph state parks according to the region of the country. How would your bar graph be different?

Histograms

Minneapolis and St. Paul are known as the Twin Cities because they are close to each other in Minnesota. Both cities are home to flourishing downtowns with tall buildings.

1. Look at the graph shown.

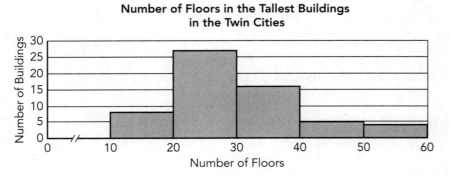

a. How is this graph different from the bar graphs you have used previously?

b. What information does the histogram display? Describe the data represented in the histogram shown. Look at the title and the labels on the axes.

c. Are the data represented in the histogram discrete or continuous? Explain your reasoning.

2. Describe the distribution of the data in terms of the overall shape and the existence of peaks, clusters, and gaps.

The graph shown is a *histogram*. A **histogram** is a graphical way to display quantitative or numerical data using vertical bars.

The width of a bar in a histogram represents an interval of data and is often referred to as a bin.

The height of the bar indicates the frequency, or the number of data values included in any given bin.

The first vertical bar in the histogram represents 8 buildings that have at least 10 floors but fewer than 20 floors.

3. Let's think about how the bars are displayed in the histogram.

   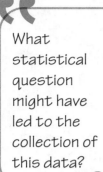

   > What statistical question might have led to the collection of this data?

   a. How many bins are shown?

   b. Are all the bins the same size?

   c. What does the height of each bar represent?

4. Describe the range of floors included in each of the remaining bins shown on the horizontal axis.

   - 2nd bin: interval 20–30

   - 3rd bin: interval 30–40

   - 4th bin: interval 40–50

   - 5th bin: interval 50–60

> In the second bin, the numbers 20 and 30 are called the *bounds* of the bin. What are the bounds of the 5th bin?

5. If a new building was constructed that had 20 floors, which bin would change? How would it change?

6. Bella says, "There are 5 buildings represented in the histogram since there are 5 bars." Do you agree or disagree with Bella's statement? If you do not agree with Bella, estimate how many buildings are represented in the histogram.

7. Can you determine how many buildings have 31 floors? Explain your reasoning.

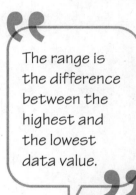

The range is the difference between the highest and the lowest data value.

8. Is it possible to determine the number of buildings that have more than 35 floors from the histogram? Why or why not?

9. Is it possible to determine the range of the data set from the histogram? Why or why not?

To create a histogram, data is usually organized into a *grouped frequency table*. A **grouped frequency table** is a table used to organize data according to how many times data values within a given range of values occur.

10. Complete the frequency table for the number of floors in the Twin Cities' tallest buildings.

Floor Intervals	Frequency (f)
10–20	
20–30	
30–40	
40–50	
50–60	

11. Write a brief summary to report the results of your data analysis about the number of floors in the Twin Cities' tallest buildings.

_____

_____

_____

_____

_____

_____

_____

_____

_____

Creating and Analyzing Histograms

New York City has over 5800 tall buildings and is home to the fifth tallest building in the United States, the Empire State Building, which is 381 meters tall. Not to be outdone, Chicago is home to the Willis Tower, formerly known as Sears Tower. It stands an impressive 442 meters tall. So how do these big cities stack up to each other? Are there any similarities or differences in the number of floors each city's 20 tallest buildings have?

The tables listing each city's 20 tallest buildings are provided at the end of the lesson. Use the tables to create grouped frequency tables and histograms for each city's tallest buildings.

1. **Complete the grouped frequency tables for the number of floors in each city's 20 tallest buildings. Then complete the histograms. Make sure that you name your tables and histograms.**

Remember, if a data value lies on one of the bounds, it should go in the bin to the right of that bound.

Number of Floors	Frequency (f)

Number of Floors	Frequency (f)

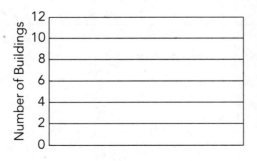

2. What is similar about the histograms? What are the differences between the two histograms?

3. Use what you know about the distributions and patterns of a graphical display to describe what the histograms say about the number of floors in each city's 20 tallest buildings.

ACTIVITY
3.3

Creating a Histogram with Continuous Data

Each year, the Empire State Building Run-Up (ESBRU) challenges runners to race up its stairs. You surveyed runners about their times at the end of the Run-Up. The results are shown in the table.

Amount of Time to Complete the ESBRU (minutes)					
10.4	11.25	15.76	9.81	12.05	18.2
10.52	13.73	13.01	12.75	14.99	11.24
15.0	15.57	16.6	14.8	13.35	12.22

1. Is the data in the table discrete or continuous? Explain your reasoning.

Shania and Trinh decide to make a histogram for the data set.
The intervals they each want to use for the histogram are shown.

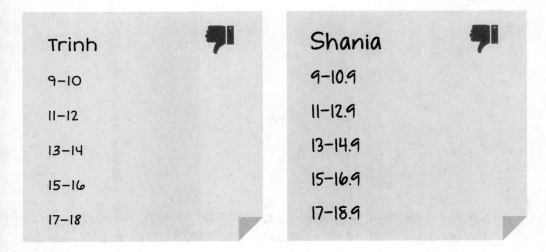

Trinh 👎
9–10
11–12
13–14
15–16
17–18

Shania 👎
9–10.9
11–12.9
13–14.9
15–16.9
17–18.9

2. Explain why both Trinh's and Shania's intervals are incorrect.
   Use a data value from the table to explain.

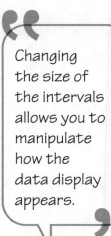

3. Create a grouped frequency table and histogram for the amount of time to complete the ESBRU.

4. Create a second grouped frequency table and histogram for the amount of time to complete the ESBRU. Use a different bin width than you used in Question 3. What do you notice?

5. What conclusions can you make about the amount of time it takes to complete the Empire State Building Run-Up? Use what you know about distributions and patterns of graphical displays.

TALK the TALK 💬

Which Plot Is Best?

Throughout this topic, you have created and analyzed a variety of numerical data displays.

1. List at least one advantage and one disadvantage of using each type of plot to display numerical data.

	Advantage (or Use)	Disadvantage (or Limitation)
dot plot		
stem-and-leaf plot		
histogram		

Use with Activity 3.2, Creating and Analyzing Histograms

New York City's 20 Tallest Buildings	
Name of Building	**Number of Floors**
One World Trade Center	104
432 Park Avenue	89
Empire State Building	103
Bank of America Tower	54
Three World Trade Center	80
Chrysler Building	77
The New York Times Building	52
One57	75
Four World Trade Center	74
70 Pine Street	66
30 Park Place	82
40 Wall Street	70
Citigroup Center	59
10 Hudson Yards	52
8 Spruce Street	76
Trump World Tower	72
30 Rockefeller Center	70
56 Leonard Street	57
CitySpire Center	75
28 Liberty Street	60

Chicago's 20 Tallest Buildings	
Name of Building	**Number of Floors**
Willis Tower	108
Trump International Hotel and Tower	98
Aon Center	83
John Hancock Center	100
Franklin Center North Tower	61
Two Prudential Plaza	64
311 South Wacker Drive	65
900 North Michigan	66
Water Tower Place	74
Aqua	82
Chase Tower	60
Park Tower	67
The Legacy at Millennium Park	73
300 North LaSalle	60
Three First National Plaza	57
Grant Thornton Tower	50
Blue Cross Blue Shield Tower	57
One Museum Park	62
Olympia Centre	63
330 North Wabash	52

Assignment

Write

Write a definition for each term in your own words.

1. histogram
2. grouped frequency table

Remember

Histograms are used when the data is numerical. Numerical data can be represented continuously in intervals.

The intervals in a histogram must all be the same size. The width of the bar represents the interval. The height of the bar indicates the frequency of values in the interval.

Practice

Jeremy's scores for the first 20 times he played the card game, *Clubs and Swords*, are listed.
50, 199, 246, 356, 89, 210, 391, 325, 273, 260, 100, 172, 123, 167, 194, 172, 23, 426, 75, 239

1. Create a frequency table and a histogram to display Jeremy's scores. Be sure to name your histogram.
2. Describe the distribution of the data. Include any specific graphical features or patterns. Explain what your answer means in terms of Jeremy's scores.
3. Create a second frequency table and histogram to provide a different view of the data distribution.

Stretch

Aviana claims that she can turn any stem-and-leaf plot into a histogram. Is she correct? Provide an example or a counterexample.

Review

1. Describe the shape of each histogram.

a.

Amusement Parks, Theme Parks, Water Parks, and Zoos in the U.S.

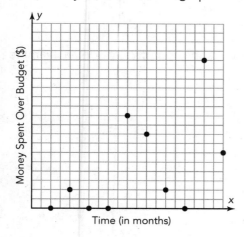

b.

Test Scores for Mr. Watson's Math Test

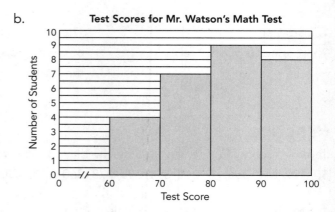

2. A free diver is diving at a constant rate of 0.75 feet per second. Write and graph an equation that represents the situation.

3. Tell a story to describe the graph.

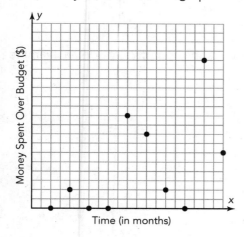

4. Determine the absolute value of each number.

a. $|-4.2|$

b. $\left|11\frac{7}{8}\right|$

The Statistical Process Summary

KEY TERMS

- variability
- data
- statistical question
- statistical process
- categorical data
- quantitative data
- population
- sample
- survey

- observational study
- experiment
- bar graph
- circle graph
- frequency
- mode
- dot plot
- distribution
- symmetric

- skewed right
- skewed left
- clusters
- gaps
- peaks
- outliers
- stem-and-leaf plot
- histogram
- grouped frequency table

LESSON 1 — What's Your Question?

Statistical problem solving begins with a statistical question. A **statistical question** is a question that anticipates an answer based on data that vary. **Data** are categories, numbers, or observations gathered in response to a statistical question. Statistics is a problem-solving process because it is about determining a possible answer to a question that has variability. In statistics, **variability** means that the value of the attribute being studied can change from one person or thing to another.

The **statistical process** has four components:

1. Formulating a statistical question.

   The statistical question posed should anticipate answers that will vary.
   Example: How many members do the clubs at my school have?
   Non-example: How many students are in the Chess Club?

2. Collecting appropriate data.

Two types of variable data that can be collected are categorical and quantitative data. **Categorical data**, or qualitative data, are data for which each piece of data fits into exactly one of several different groups or categories. **Quantitative data**, or numerical data, are data for which each piece of data can be placed on a numerical scale and compared.

A statistical question can be answered by collecting data from an entire population or, more commonly, from a sample of the population. A **population** is an entire set of items from which data are collected. A **sample** is a selection from a population.

Three common methods of data collection are surveys, observational studies, and experiments. In a **survey,** people are asked one or more questions. Similarly, in an **observational study**, the researcher collects data by observing the variable of interest. In an **experiment**, the researcher imposes a condition and observes the results.

3. Analyzing the data graphically and numerically.

After you collect the data, it is time to analyze and interpret the results. Analysis includes selecting the most appropriate graphical display and numerical summaries for your question and your method of data collection.

A **bar graph** displays categorical data using either horizontal or vertical bars on a graph. The height or length of each bar indicates the value for that category.

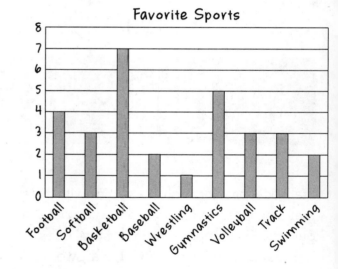

A **circle graph**, often called a pie chart, displays categorical data using sectors, or "wedges," of a circle. It shows how parts of the whole relate to the whole and how parts of the whole relate to the other parts. The area of each sector corresponds to the percentage of the part in relation to the whole.

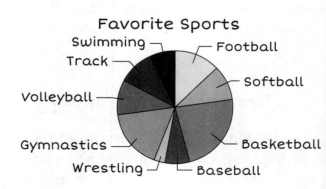

To create graphs, you can determine the frequency of each response to a statistical question and record the frequencies in a frequency table. A **frequency** is the number of times an item or number occurs in a data set. Once the frequency is known, you can determine the mode. The **mode** is the value or values that occur most frequently in a data set.

4. Interpreting the results of the analysis.

You can use your analysis to make conclusions about the data. For example, from the graphs and table above you can conclude that basketball is the most popular sport among those that were surveyed.

Sport	Frequency (f)
Football	4
Softball	3
Basketball	7
Baseball	2
Wrestling	1
Gymnastics	5
Volleyball	3
Track	3
Swimming	2

One way to describe a set of quantitative data is by drawing a graphical display of the data.

A **dot plot** is a data display that shows discrete data on a number line with dots, Xs, or other symbols. Dot plots help organize and display a small number of data points.

In this example of a dot plot, the number line represents the number of gold medals won by countries in the 2014 Winter Olympics. Each X above a number represents a country that won that many gold medals.

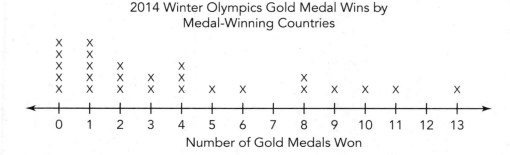

2014 Winter Olympics Gold Medal Wins by
Medal-Winning Countries

Number of Gold Medals Won

When you analyze a graphical representation of numeric data, you can look at its shape, center, and spread to draw conclusions.

The overall shape of a graph is called the distribution of data. A **distribution** is the way in which the data are spread out. The shape of the distribution can reveal a lot of information about data. There are many different distributions, but the most common are **symmetric**, **skewed right**, and **skewed left**.

When analyzing a graphical display of data, you can also look for any interesting patterns. Some of these patterns include:

- **clusters**—areas where data are grouped close together
- **gaps**—areas where there are no data
- **peaks**—values that contain more data points than the values on either side of it
- **outliers**—data values that lie a large distance from the other data. Outliers usually accompany gaps in data.

Shapes of Typical Distribution of Graphical Displays of Data

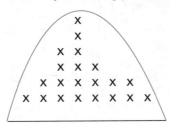

symmetric

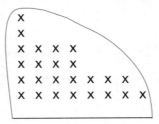

skewed right

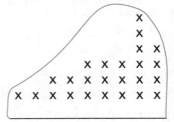

skewed left

- The left and right halves of the graph are mirror images of each other.
- The peak is in the middle, because there are many data values in the center.

- The peak of the data is to the left side of the graph.
- There are only a few data points to the right side of the graph.

- The peak of the data is to the right side of the graph.
- There are only a few data points to the left side of the graph.

**Total Medals Won by Countries
2016 Summer Olympics**

```
 0 | 5 5 5 6 6 6 7 7 7 8 8 8 8 8 9 9
 1 | 0 0 0 1 1 1 1 1 3 3 5 5 7 8 8 8 9 9
 2 | 2 8 9
 3 |
 4 | 1 2 2
 5 | 6
 6 | 7
 7 | 0
 8 |
 9 |
10 |
11 |
12 | 1
```

Key: 4|1 = 41 medals won.

A **stem-and-leaf plot** is a graphical method used to represent ordered numerical data sets with a larger range of data values. Once the data is ordered, the stem and leaves are determined. Typically, the stem is all the digits in a number except the rightmost digit, which is the leaf.

A **histogram** is a graphical way to display quantitative or numerical data using vertical bars. The numerical data are represented continuously with intervals. The intervals in a histogram must all be the same size. The width of a bar in a histogram represents the interval. The height of the bar indicates the frequency, or the number of data values, in the interval.

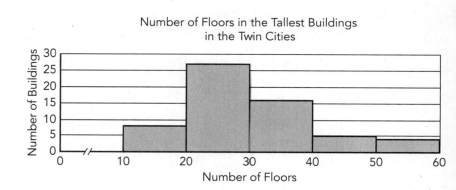

Number of Floors in the Tallest Buildings in the Twin Cities

Dot plots show individual data values. Histograms display grouped data. For example, you cannot determine from the histogram how many buildings have 21 floors, or more than 45 floors.

Floor Intervals	Frequency (f)
10–20	8
20–30	27
30–40	16
40–50	5
50–60	4

To create a histogram, data is usually organized into a grouped frequency table. A **grouped frequency table** is a table used to organize data according to how many times data values within a given range of values occur.

For example, this grouped frequency table displays the data represented by the histogram above.

Numerical Summaries of Data

The size of vertebrates varies widely, from blue whales at the large end to tiny frogs at the small end.

Carnegie Learning Family Guide

Module 5: Describing Variability of Quantities

TOPIC 2: NUMERICAL SUMMARIES OF DATA

In this topic, students learn about measures of central tendency and measures of variability and when each is the most appropriate measure for a given data set. Students may have an informal or intuitive understanding of "average," but this topic formalizes the ideas of the mean and median of a data set. They learn that the median is the middle value in a data set and that the mean can be thought of as a fair share or the balance point of a data set. From there, students learn about measures of variability, specifically the interquartile range and mean absolute deviation. Students analyze data sets, selecting the most appropriate measures of central tendency and measures of variability.

Where have we been?

In prior grades, students determined which value in a data set occurred the most. This measure is the mode. Students build on that as they learn about other measures of central tendency: the median and the mean. When students learned about division, they created equal groups, which is a similar construct to mean as "fair share."

Where are we going?

This topic provides students with the building blocks of numerical data analysis: calculating measures of central tendency and measures of variability to describe data. Students will continue to use these computations, and the reasoning behind them, as they compare data distributions in grade 7.

Using Models to Determine the Mean of a Data Set

The model shows how fair shares can be used to visualize the mean of a data set. For example, this simplified data set shows 2 and 6. By moving 2 from the stack of 6 to the stack of 2, the data are evenly distributed, with 4 in each stack. Thus, the mean of 2 and 6 is 4.

TOPIC 2: Family Guide • M5-69

Myth: Some students are "right-brain" learners while other students are "left-brain" learners.

As you probably know, the brain is divided into two hemispheres: the left and the right. Some categorize people by their preferred or dominant mode of thinking. "Right-brain" thinkers are considered to be more intuitive, creative, and imaginative. "Left-brain" thinkers are more logical, verbal, and mathematical.

The brain can also be broken down into *lobes*. The *occipital lobe* can be found in back of the brain, and it is responsible for processing visual information. The *temporal lobes*, which sit above your ears, process language and sensory information. A band across the top of your head is the *parietal lobe*, and it controls movement. Finally, the *frontal lobe* is where planning and learning occurs. Another way to think about the brain is from the back to the front, where information goes from highly concrete to abstract.

Why don't we claim that some people are "back of the brain" thinkers who are highly concrete; whereas, others are "frontal thinkers" who are more abstract? The reason is that the brain is a highly interconnected organ. Each lobe hands off information to be processed by other lobes, and they are constantly talking to each other. All of us are *whole-brain thinkers!*

#mathmythbusted

Talking Points

You can support your student's learning by asking questions about the work they do in class or at home. Your student is learning about the process of framing questions about data and representing data numerically.

Questions to Ask

- How does this problem look like something you did in class?
- Can you show me the strategy you used to solve this problem? Do you know another way to solve it?
- Does your answer make sense? Why?
- Is there anything you don't understand? How can you use today's lesson to help?

Key Terms

median
The median is the middle number in a data set when the values are placed in order from least to greatest.

mean
The mean is the arithmetic average of the numbers in a data set.

range
The range is the difference between the maximum and minimum values of a data set.

In the Middle 1

Analyzing Data Using Measures of Center

WARM UP

Simplify each numeric expression.

1. $(13 + 17) \div 2$

2. $(29 + 36) \div 2$

3. $(48 + 9) \div 2$

4. $(27 + 31) \div 2$

LEARNING GOALS

- Define the three measures of center: mode, median, and mean.
- Recognize that a measure of center for a numerical data set is a single value that summarizes all of its values.
- Give quantitative measures of center for a data set, including mean and/or median, and interpret the mode, median, and mean for a data set.

KEY TERMS

- measure of center
- mode
- median
- balance point
- mean

You have analyzed, created, and interpreted data displays such as dot plots, stem-and-leaf plots, and histograms. You have described shapes and patterns in distributions of data displays. How can you describe a numerical data set as a single value?

Describing Data

Analyze each display. Identify the most typical value and estimate the middle value in each.

> What patterns do you notice in the data?

1.

Pencils in Backpacks

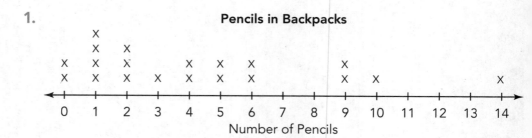

Number of Pencils

2. **Ages of U.S. First Ladies (20th Century)**

3	1
4	0 3 4 5 7 8 9
5	0 2 4 6 6 6 9
6	0 0 3

Key: 6|0 means 60.

3. **Hours Spent Playing Video Games on Weekends**

When you analyze a set of data, you often want to describe it numerically. One way to numerically describe a data set is to use a *measure of center*.

There are three measures that describe how a data set is centered: the *mean*, the *median*, and the *mode*.

The **mode** is the data value or values that occur most frequently in a data set.

The **median** is the middle number in a data set when the values are placed in order from least to greatest or greatest to least. When a data set has an odd number of data values, you can determine which number is exactly in the middle of the data set. If there is an even number of data values, then the median is calculated by adding the two middle numbers and dividing by 2.

> A **measure of center** tells you how the data values are clustered, or where the "center" of a graph of the data is located.

> A data set can have more than one mode.

1. The Olive Street Middle School girls' basketball team has a chance to be in the league playoffs. Coach Harris must determine which of the following 3 players should get more playing time in the first playoff game. In the past six games, Josephine scored 12, 12, 6, 26, 4, and 12 points. Shelly scored 3, 2, 8, 17, 10, and 20 points. Chanice scored 15, 12, 13, 10, 8, and 14 points.

   a. Determine the mode for the number of points scored by each player.

   b. Determine the median number of points scored by each player.

c. Which of these two measures of center, mode or median, would be better for Coach Harris to use in making her decision? Explain your reasoning.

2. Explain what Lamar did incorrectly to determine that the median was 10. Then determine the correct median.

Lamar says that the median is 10 for the data set 5, 6, 10, 4, and 9.

A Third Measure: Mean as Fair Share

There is a third measure of center that can describe the values in a data set. This measure of center is called the mean and is based on leveling off or creating fair shares.

WORKED EXAMPLE

Analyze the two stacks of cubes.

If you were to create two equal stacks of cubes, you would subtract two cubes from the greater stack, and add the two cubes to the lesser stack. In doing so, you have created two equal stacks.

1. Analyze each stack of cubes shown. Create four equal stacks of cubes. Record what operations you performed.

a. 2, 3, 5, 6

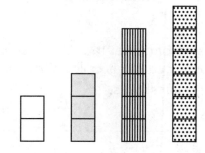

b. 2, 3, 5, 10

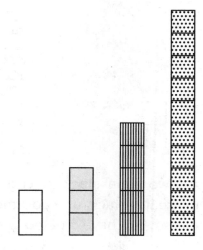

You have to keep the number of stacks the same.

2. Compare your results from parts (a) and (b). How did the number of cubes in each equal stack change in part (b)? Explain why this happened.

A Third Measure: Mean as Balancing

In the previous activity, data values were represented by stacks of cubes. You rearranged the stacks to create equal stacks, or fair shares. You can also represent quantities on a number line and create a *balance point*.

WORKED EXAMPLE

Consider the data set: 2, 6.

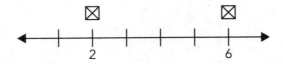

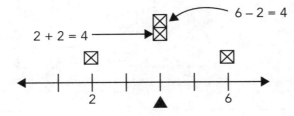

The value 2 was moved to the right from 2 to 4. To maintain balance, 6 was moved 2 to the left from 6 to 4. The balance point is 4.

When you are attempting to create a balance on a number line, if you move a value to the right a certain amount, then you must also move a value to the left that amount. You can move a data value to the left and right as much as you like as long as you do the opposite to another data value. You can start however you like.

1. **What do you think the ▲ represents?**

> When you have all the points at the same value, the number line is balanced. The value where the number line is balanced is called the **balance point**.

You can also determine the balance point of a number line with more than two data points.

2. Kathryn determined the balance point of the data set. Record the operations she used on the blank lines in each step. Label the balance point in Step 3.

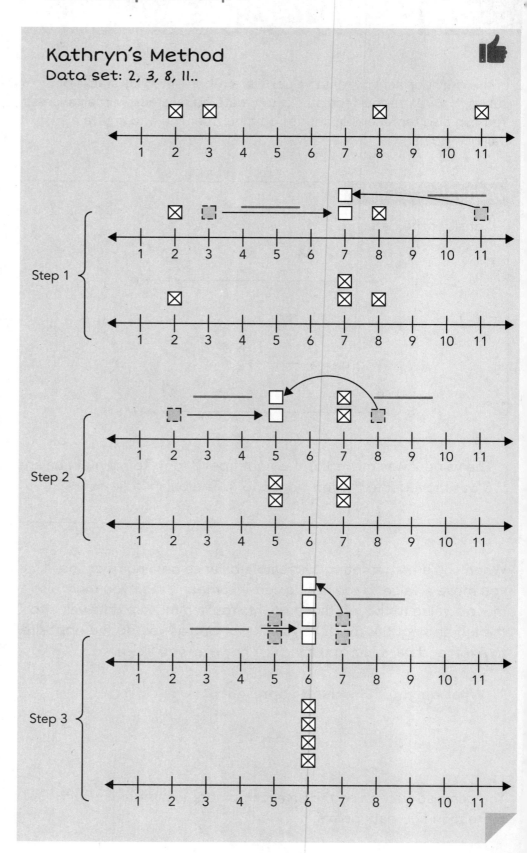

Kathryn's Method
Data set: 2, 3, 8, 11..

Step 1

Step 2

Step 3

Recall the data sets for the number of points each player scored for the Olive Street Middle School Basketball team.

3. For each data set, determine the balance point on the number lines shown. Record the steps you used to determine the balance point.

a. Josephine
   Data set: 12, 12, 6, 26, 4, 12

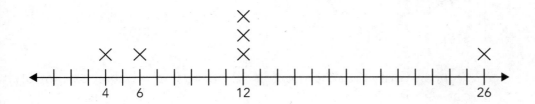

b. Shelly
   Data set: 3, 2, 8, 17, 10, 20

c. Chanice
   Data set: 15, 12, 13, 10, 8, 14

The balance point can also be called the *mean*. The **mean** is the arithmetic average of the numbers in a data set.

> **WORKED EXAMPLE**
>
> The mean is calculated by adding all of the values in the data set and dividing the sum by the number of values.
>
> The mean of the data set for the points Josephine scored is calculated by:
>
> **Step 1:** 12 + 12 + 6 + 26 + 4 + 12 = 72
>
> **Step 2:** $\frac{72}{6} = 12$
>
> You can verify that the mean is 12 because the balance point of the data set is 12.

The expression 72 ÷ 6 takes the 72 total points and divides them evenly into 6 games, for 12 points in each game.

4. **Calculate the mean number of points scored by each player.**

   a. **Josephine**
      Data set: 12, 12, 6, 26, 4, 12

   b. **Shelly**
      Data set: 3, 2, 8, 17, 10, 20

   b. **Chanice**
      Data set: 15, 12, 13, 10, 8, 14

A corporation is awarding grants to local schools to purchase fitness equipment. The principal at Sharpe Middle School would like to submit an application for the grant. If awarded the money, the school would like to add fitness equipment to the gym.

Before she submits the application, the principal wants to understand how much time the students at Sharpe Middle School spend exercising each weekday. She decides to give a survey to 15 anonymous students. The results are shown.

Statistical Process
• Formulate Question
• Collect Data
• Graph and Analyze
• Interpret

0 minutes	40 minutes	60 minutes	30 minutes	60 minutes
10 minutes	45 minutes	30 minutes	300 minutes	90 minutes
30 minutes	120 minutes	60 minutes	0 minutes	20 minutes

1. **Identify the statistical question posed in this situation. Create a display from the survey data. Calculate and interpret each measure of center. Then write a summary statement based on your findings.**

TALK the TALK

Describing a Numerical Data Set as a Single Value

In this lesson you learned about three measures of center: mode, median, and mean.

1. Describe how you can use each measure of center to describe a data set.

2. What are the most important differences between each of the measures of center?

3. Which is your favorite measure of center? Why?

Assignment

Write

Choose a word to best complete each sentence.

> measure of center   mode   median   mean   balance point

1. A _____ for a numerical data set summarizes all of its values with a single number.

2. The _____ is the arithmetic average of the numbers in a data set.

3. When you have all the points on a number line at the same value after moving data values, this value is called the _____.

4. The _____ is the middle number in a data set when the values are placed in order from least to greatest.

5. The _____ is the data value or values that occur most frequently in a data set.

Remember

There are three measures of center: mode, median, and mean. Measures of center are numerical ways of determining where the center of data is located.

Practice

1. Determine the mode and median for each data set. What does each measure of center tell you about the data set?

   a. The heights of each of your classmates in inches are 62, 58, 67, 68, 68, 72, 66, 65, 60, 61, 64, 67, and 64.

   b. Yolanda made golf putts from distances of 7 feet, 15 feet, 8 feet, 9.5 feet, and 11 feet from the hole.

   c. Everyone in your class reaches into their pockets to see how much change they have. The amounts, in cents, are 15, 48, 92, 72, 50, 75, 70, 18, 85, 95, 42, 25, 63, 59, 87, 13, 55, 75, 99, and 25.

2. Ms. Zhang's math class has had 5 quizzes, each worth 10 points. Julian and his friends, Mona and Timi, are determining who did the best on the quizzes. Their scores are:

   Julian: 3, 9, 9, 9, 10

   Mona: 6, 7, 7, 10, 10

   Timi: 6, 7, 8, 9, 10

   a. According to the mode, who did the best on the quizzes? Is the mode a good way to determine who did best on the quizzes? Why or why not?

   b. According to the median, who did the best on the quizzes? Is the median a good way to determine who did best on the the quizzes? Why or why not?

c. Determine the mean score by leveling off. Show diagrams and record your operations.

d. Determine each student's mean by determining the balance point. Show your steps on a number line and record your operations.

e. Calculate each students mean score.

f. Who would you say did best on the quizzes? Explain your choice.

3. The rate at which crickets chirp is affected by the temperature. In fact, you can estimate the outside temperature by counting cricket chirps. As a homework assignment, Mr. Ortega asks each of his students to count the number of chirps they hear in 15 seconds at 8:00 pm. The results are shown.

36, 37, 41, 39, 35, 39, 35, 39, 42, 37, 40, 35, 36, 37, 42, 35, 37, 37, 38, 42, 41, 37, 41

a. Determine the mode for the number of chirps heard in 15 seconds.

b. What does the mode tell you about the number of chirps heard in 15 seconds?

c. Determine the median number of chirps heard in 15 seconds.

d. What does the median tell you about the number of chirps heard in 15 seconds?

e. Calculate the mean number of chirps heard by the students in 15 seconds.

f. What does the mean tell you about the number of chirps heard in 15 seconds?

4. An estimate of the temperature outside can be calculated by adding 40 to the number of cricket chirps you hear in 15 seconds. Chelsea used a sample of six calculated chirps:

76, 74, 74, 76, 73, 77

a. Use a number line to determine the balance point to estimate the mean number of chirps. Then, describe the steps you took to determine the balance point.

b. Calculate the mean from the data values. How does it compare to your answer from part (a)?

Stretch

1. Create a data set where the mean is greater than the median.
2. Create a data set where the mean is less than the median.

Review

1. Describe the shape of the distribution of the data shown.

a. 1|4 = 14

1	4
2	0 1
3	2 2 9
4	1 4 5 6 7
5	3 5 7 7

b. 4|1 = 4.1

4	1
5	3 7 8
6	0 1 4 4
7	1 3 4 7
8	0 9 9
9	6

2. The graph represents the total distance traveled in miles. Use the graph to answer each question.

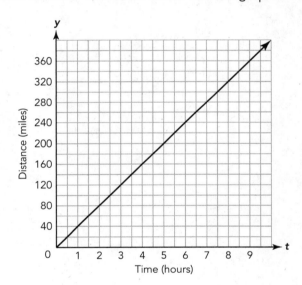

a. Write an equation to represent the graph. Define each variable.

b. If you know the number of hours, how can you use the graph to determine any total distance? How many hours did it take to travel 120 miles?

3. Evaluate each expression.

a. $\dfrac{(8 + 2)^2}{2}$

b. $10 + 5^2 - 3 \cdot 2^2$

Box It Up

Displaying the Five-Number Summary

2

WARM UP

The scores from an English quiz are displayed in the stem-and-leaf plot.

Stem	Leaf
4	0
5	8
6	1
7	2
8	3 4 5
9	2 3

Key
5|8 = 58%

1. What is the median of the data?
2. What does the median describe in the problem situation?

LEARNING GOALS

- Give quantitative measures of variation, including interquartile range, and interpret the range, quartiles, and interquartile range as measures of variation for a data set.
- Calculate and interpret the five-number summary as a measure of variation for a data set.
- Display numerical data in box plots.
- Describe an overall pattern of data with reference to the context in which the data were gathered.

KEY TERMS

- measures of variation
- range
- quartile
- interquartile range (IQR)
- box-and-whisker plot

Mean, median, and mode are used to describe measures of center for a data set. Other characteristics are also important, such as how much the data varies from that center. How can you use mathematics to describe the variation in a data set?

Human Box Plot

You teacher will provide you with an index card and a penny. On the index card, write the date imprinted on the penny.

1. Consider the data from the class and predict the shape of the data set. Do you think that it will be skewed right, skewed left, or symmetrical? Do you think that there will be any clusters or gaps?

On your teacher's signal, line up with your index card from oldest date to the most recent date. As a class, discuss how to determine the following measures.

2. Complete the table for your data set.

Minimum	Lower Quartile (Q1)	Median	Upper Quartile (Q3)	Maximum

3. Use what you learned in this activity to write descriptions of each term.

   a. minimum

   b. lower quartile (Q1)

   c. median

   d. upper quartile (Q3)

   e. maximum

The 5-Number Summary

Given the collection of pennies provided by your teacher, line up the pennies from the earliest imprinted date to the most recent.

1. **Describe the variation of the data.**

A **measure of variation** describes the spread of data values. One measure of variation is the *range*. The **range** is the difference between the maximum and minimum values of a data set.

2. **Identify the minimum and maximum values of the data set.**

3. **Calculate the range for the penny data.**

Another set of values that helps to describe variation in a data set is a *quartile*. When data in a set is arranged in order, **quartiles** are the numbers that split data into quarters (or fourths).

Quartiles are often denoted by the letter Q followed by a number that indicates which fourth it represents. Since the median is the second quartile, it could be denoted Q2. The other quartiles are Q1 and Q3.

4. How do you calculate the quartiles for a data set?

5. How many quartiles does it take to divide the data into fourths?

In your workspace, divide your pennies into quartiles, leaving a space for each.

6. Identify the value of each quartile for the penny data in your group.

   a. Q1   b. Q2

   c. Q3

7. For each quartile, identify what percent of the data is below the quartile and what percent of the data is above the quartile.

	below	above

a. Q1

b. Q2

c. Q3

8. What percent of the data is between Q1 and Q3?

The **interquartile range**, abbreviated **IQR**, is the difference between the third quartile, Q3, and the first quartile, Q1. The IQR indicates the range of the middle 50 percent of the data.

9. What do you think is meant by the middle 50 percent?

10. Do you think it is possible for two sets of data to have the same range, but different IQRs? Explain your reasoning.

11. What is the IQR for your penny data?

To summarize and describe the spread of the data values, you can use the five-number summary. The five-number summary includes these 5 values from a data set:

- Minimum: the least value in the data set
- Q1: the first quartile
- Median: the median of the data set
- Q3: the third quartile
- Maximum: the greatest value in a data set.

12. Determine the 5-number summary and IQR for each data set. Explain the process you used to calculate the values and what they tell you about the data.

a. 24, 32, 16, 18, 30, 20

b. 200, 150, 260, 180, 300, 240, 280

ACTIVITY 2.2

Box-and-Whisker Plots

There is a special type of graph that displays the variation in a data set. A **box-and-whisker plot**, or just box plot, is a graph that displays the five-number summary of a data set.

Examine the box-and-whisker plot shown.

WORKED EXAMPLE

Recall that the five-number summary consists of:

- minimum value in the data set
- Q1
- median
- Q3
- maximum value in the data set

Parts of a Box-and-Whisker Plot

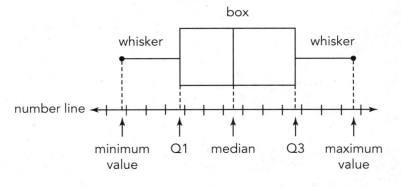

---

1. **What does the "box" in the box-and-whisker plot represent? What do the "whiskers" represent?**

Box-and-whisker plots can be represented horizontally and vertically.

2. Use the box-and-whisker plot shown to answer each question.

Number of Points Scored on a Math Test

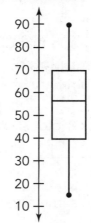

a. Identify the given values for the points scored on the math test. Then, explain what those values tell you about the scores on the test.

- minimum: • Q1:

- median: • Q3:

- maximum: • range:

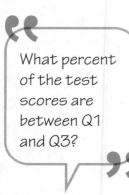

What percent of the test scores are between Q1 and Q3?

b. Determine the IQR for the test scores. Then, explain what the IQR represents in this problem situation.

c. How many students took the math test? Explain your answer.

d. Karyn says the median should be at 50 because it is in the middle of the number line. Do you agree with Karyn's claim? Explain how you determined your answer.

e. Jamal claims that more students scored between 15 and 40 than between 70 and 90 because the lower whisker is longer than the upper whisker. Do you agree or disagree with Jamal? Explain your reasoning.

You can describe the distribution of a box plot in the same way you described the shapes of stem-and-leaf plots or histograms.

3. How would you describe the distribution of the box plot? Why?

4. Create a box-and-whisker plot to represent the penny data. First, recall the values of the five-number summary.

a. minimum:

b. Q1:

c. median:

d. Q3:

e. maximum:

Building a Box Plot

- Label the number line. Include the maximum and minimum values.
- Place dots above the minimum and maximum values.
- Place vertical lines above the median and quartile values. Draw the box around them.
- Draw lines, or whiskers, to connect the box to the minimum and maximum values.
- Name the box-and-whisker plot.

5. Use the number line shown to complete the box-and-whisker plot.

a. Describe the distribution of the box plot.

b. How do the lengths of the whiskers compare? Describe why you think this is so.

6. Think about the line of pennies that you created when you ordered them by imprinted dates and separated them into quartiles.

a. How many pennies were below Q1? How many pennies were above Q3?

b. Do these values match the length of the whiskers on your box-and-whisker plot?

7. Summarize what you can determine about the penny data by examining the box plot.

Comparing Box-and-Whisker Plots

A newspaper reporter is writing an investigative story about the wait time at two local restaurants. With the help of her assistant, the reporter randomly selected 11 patrons at each restaurant and recorded how many minutes they had to wait before being served. The results are shown.

1. Create a vertical box-and-whisker plot for the wait times at each of the restaurants. Use the same number line for each representation so that they can be compared.

2. Describe the distributions of each box plot.

3. What is the range of wait times? What does the five-number summary tell you about the spread of the data that the range does not tell you?

Wait Time (minutes)

The Captain's Corner	
16	60
22	15
12	24
20	18
16	23
22	

The First Deck	
34	60
44	10
27	52
26	31
47	48
45	

4. What do the IQR values tell you about the time spent waiting at each restaurant?

5. How does the mean wait time compare to the median wait time for each restaurant?

6. Assume the food prices and service were the same in both restaurants. Write a brief summary to report the results of your data analysis back to the newspaper reporter to help answer their question about wait times in The Captain's Corner and The First Deck restaurants.

_____

_____

_____

_____

_____

_____

_____

_____

_____

TALK the TALK

Build a Box

1. Analyze the box-and-whisker plot shown. Determine if each statement is true or false and provide a reason for your decision.

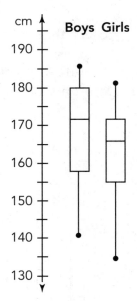

a. On average, the girls are taller.

b. The range of heights is greater for the boys.

c. Half the girls are over 165 cm tall.

d. Half the boys are over 172 cm tall.

e. The shortest person is a boy.

f. The tallest person is a boy.

2. Use the given information to determine a five-number summary and construct a box-and-whisker plot. Is your data set the only possible solution? Why or why not?

- The data set has a range of 30.

- The maximum value is 50.

- The IQR is 10.

- The median is closer to Q1 than to Q3.

3. Create a data set to represent the box-and-whisker plot shown. Is your data set the only possible solution? Why or why not?

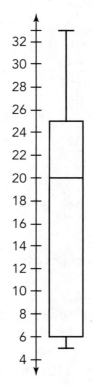

a. Data set with 11 numbers.

b. Data set with 8 numbers.

Assignment

Write

Write the term that best completes each statement.

range	quartiles	interquartile range	five-number summary

1. The _____ is the difference between the first quartile and the third quartile.

2. The _____ for a set of data is the difference between the maximum and minimum values.

3. _____ are values that divide a data set into four equal parts once the data are arranged in ascending order.

4. A(n) _____ lists the minimum and maximum values, the median, and the quartiles for a set of data.

Remember

To summarize and describe the spread of data values, you can use a five-number summary. A five-number summary includes 5 values from a data set:

- Minimum: the least value in the data set
- Q1: the first quartile, or the median of the lower half of data
- Median: the median of the data set
- Q3: the third quartile, or the median of the upper half of data
- Maximum: the greatest value in a data set.

The representation of a five-number summary is called a box-and-whisker plot, or simply a box plot.

Practice

1. The box-and-whisker plot shows the distribution of scores on a history quiz.

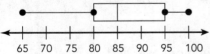

    65 70 75 80 85 90 95 100

    a. Identify the median of the data and interpret its meaning.
    b. Identify the range of the data and interpret its meaning.

2. Answer each question using the data set: 0, 5, 5, 15, 30, 30, 45, 50, 50, 60, 75, 110, 140, 240, 330.

    a. Sketch a box-and-whisker plot.
    b. What is the median for the data set?
    c. What is Q3 for the data set?

3. Answer each question using the data set: 10, 10, 10, 10, 35, 75, 90, 95, 100, 175, 420, 490, 515, 515, 790.

    a. Sketch a box-and-whisker plot.

    b. What do you notice about this box-and-whisker plot?

    c. What is the median for the data set?

4. The residents of Summersville, West Virginia, are concerned about people speeding through their town on US Route 19. The police decide to monitor the speed of the cars that pass through the town at various times during the day. The data show the recorded speeds in miles per hour of 23 cars at 7:30 am on one Wednesday morning.

    73, 68, 72, 61, 51, 68, 70, 53, 72, 71, 46, 51, 55, 53, 65, 57, 65, 57, 58, 68, 61, 48, 83

    a. What is the range of data?

    b. Construct a box-and-whisker plot of the data.

    c. Interpret each number in the five-number summary.

    d. What does the IQR value tell you about the speeds of the cars?

    e. If the speed limit through the town is 50 miles per hour, should the residents be concerned based on this data?

5. San Francisco, California, and Richmond, Virginia, are located at about the same latitude on opposite sides of the United States. The table shows the amount of rainfall each city gets on average each month.

	Jan.	Feb.	Mar.	Apr.	May	Jun.	Jul.	Aug.	Sep.	Oct.	Nov.	Dec.
San Francisco, CA	4.4 in.	3.3 in.	3.1 in.	1.4 in.	0.3 in.	0.1 in.	0.0 in.	0.1 in.	0.3 in.	1.3 in.	2.9 in.	3.1 in.
Richmond, VA	3.3 in.	3.3 in.	3.6 in.	3.0 in.	3.8 in.	3.6 in.	5.0 in.	4.4 in.	3.3 in.	3.5 in.	3.3 in.	3.3 in.

    a. Calculate and interpret the range of rainfall for each city.

    b. Construct box-and-whisker plots for the average rainfall for each city on the same graph.

    c. Compare the rainfall in San Francisco and Richmond. Describe the shape of each box plot.

    d. Interpret the IQR for the rainfall in each city.

Stretch

An arithmetic sequence is formed by adding (or subtracting) the same number over and over.

For example, 2, 5, 8, 11, 14, 17 . . . is an arithmetic sequence formed by adding 3 over and over after choosing a starting number.

1. Create box-and-whisker plots using different arithmetic sequences as data.

2. How are the plots similar?

3. What do you notice about the IQR of each plot?

Review

1. Determine the mean, median, mode, and range of the set of data. Round your answers to the nearest hundredth when necessary.
   a. 14, 19, 8, 22, 11, 19, 4, 18, 12, 10, 21
   b. 55, 24, 73, 108, 39, 46, 72, 100, 92, 32

2. Construct a dot plot for each.
   a. Display the number of items purchased by a number of randomly chosen customers at a toy store. The data are 2, 4, 3, 7, 12, 3, 1, 5, 6, 3, 4, 2, 4, 3, 7, 14, 10, 3, 5, and 9. Describe the distribution.
   b. Display the scores on a recent math quiz. The data are 12, 14, 8, 13, 12, 14, 5, 13, 14, 3, 15, 15, 10, 13, 12, 0, 14, 11, 14, 13, and 10. Describe the distribution.

3. Determine each product.
   a. $\frac{3}{8} \times \frac{4}{5}$
   b. $\frac{1}{2} \times \frac{2}{1}$

March MADness

Mean Absolute Deviation

3

WARM UP

Determine the absolute value of each number.

1. $|-4|$
2. $|12.5|$
3. $|-1.09|$
4. $|4\frac{2}{3}|$

LEARNING GOALS

- Determine the absolute deviations of data points in a data set.
- Give quantitative measures of variation, including mean absolute deviation, for a data set.
- Use the mean absolute deviation as a measure of variation to describe and interpret data.
- Compare data sets using variation and the mean absolute deviation.
- Summarize numerical data sets in relation to their context.

KEY TERMS

- deviation
- absolute deviation
- mean absolute deviation

The interquartile range is used as a measure of variation when the median is the measure of center. How can you measure the variation when mean is the measure of center?

We Are the Champions

Coach Harris's basketball team is advancing to the district championship. Tamika and Lynn are possible starters for the game. Dot plots for each player's scoring over the past six games are shown.

Number of Points Scored by Tamika

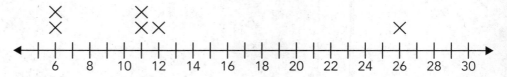

Number of Points Scored by Lynn

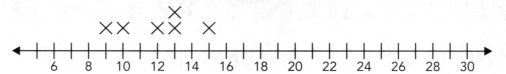

1. Determine the mean of each data set. Explain what this number tells you.

2. How are the two data sets similar and different?

3. Explain why the two data sets have the same mean.

Previously, you examined the dot plots of two basketball players–Tamika and Lynn. Coach Harris needs to choose between Tamika and Lynn as starters for the game.

Number of Points Scored by Tamika

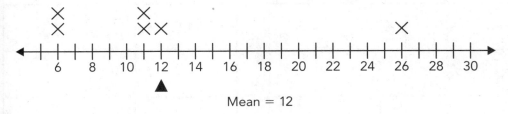

Mean = 12

Number of Points Scored by Lynn

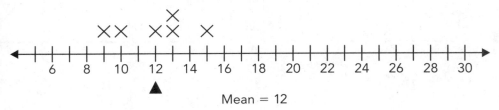

Mean = 12

1. **Based on the dot plots, which player do you think Coach Harris should choose?**

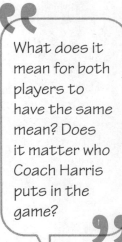

> What does it mean for both players to have the same mean? Does it matter who Coach Harris puts in the game?

When analyzing a data set, measures of center give you an idea of where the data is centered, or what a typical data value might be. There is another measure that can help you analyze data. Measures of variation describe the spread of the data values. Just as there are several measures of central tendency, there are also several measures of variation.

The **deviation** of a data value indicates how far that data value is from the mean. To calculate the deviation, subtract the mean from the data value:

deviation = data value − mean

Collect the data!

2. Describe the deviations. Record your results in the tables.

Tamika		Lynn	
Points Scored	Describe the Deviation from the Mean	Points Scored	Describe the Deviation from the Mean
11		15	
11		12	
6		13	
26		10	
6		9	
12		13	

3. What is the meaning if a deviation is positive? Is negative? Is 0?

4. What do you notice about the deviations for each player?

5. Carly claims that the sum of the deviations for a data set will always be 0. Do you agree? Why or why not?

The sum of all the deviations less than 0 is equal to the sum of the deviations greater than 0. Because the mean is the balance point, the sums of data points on either side of the balance point are equal to each other.

In order to get an idea of the spread of the data values, you can take the absolute value of each deviation and then determine the mean of those absolute values. The absolute value of each deviation is called the **absolute deviation**. The **mean absolute deviation** (MAD) is the mean of the absolute deviations.

6. Record the absolute deviations for the points scored in the tables.

Tamika				Lynn		
Points Scored	Deviation from the Mean	Absolute Deviation		Points Scored	Deviation from the Mean	Absolute Deviation
11	−1			15	3	
11	−1			12	0	
6	−6			13	1	
26	14			10	−2	
6	−6			9	−3	
12	0			13	1	

7. Calculate the mean absolute deviation for the points scored for each player.

8. What does the mean absolute deviation tell you about the points scored by each player?

9. If you were Coach Harris, which player would you choose to play in the championship game? Justify your decision.

"
What statistical question can I ask about this data?
"

Variation in Non-Numeric Data

Sometimes you can change non-numerical data into numeric data in order to analyze it. Consider, for example, the report cards shown. Grades for the courses are assigned to the categories A, B, C, D, and F, with A being the highest grade.

Luca	
Science	B
Cultural Literacy	A
Music	C
Math	A
English	B

Eric	
Math	A
English	B
Cultural Literacy	C
Science	A
Music	A

1. Explain how you can change the report card data into numeric data.

2. Determine the mean of each data set. What does each mean tell you?

3. Determine the mean absolute deviation for each data set.

Luca			Eric		
Data Value	Describe the Deviation from the Mean	Absolute Deviation	Data Value	Describe the Deviation from the Mean	Absolute Deviation

4. Interpret each of the mean absolute deviations.

The tables on the next page show the heights in inches of ten NBA basketball players and ten 6th-grade basketball players.

1. Write a statistical question you can answer by analyzing the data.

2. Create a dot plot for each data set.

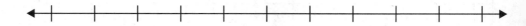

3. Complete each table. Then, compare the data sets and interpret your results.

NBA Players		
Height (in.)	Describe the Deviation from the Mean	Absolute Deviation
79		
74		
78		
81		
81		
76		
84		
80		
82		
83		

6th-Grade Players		
Height (in.)	Describe the Deviation from the Mean	Absolute Deviation
68		
64		
60		
58		
62		
65		
64		
60		
61		
65		

Mean absolute deviation and interquartile range are both measures of variation.

TALK the TALK

IQR and MAD

1. Create vertical box plots and calculate the interquartile ranges for the data sets in the previous activity.

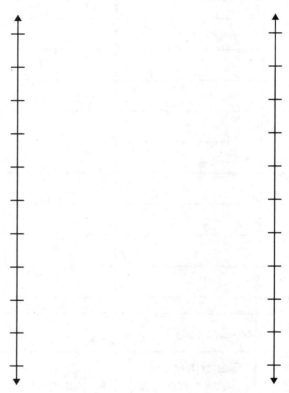

2. Compare the mean absolute deviations and the interquartile ranges.

   a. What does each measure tell you about the data set?

   b. How are they the same? How are they different?

Assignment

Write

Complete each sentence with the correct term.

| Absolute deviation | Mean absolute deviation | Measures of variation | Deviation |

1. _____ describe(s) the spread of the data values.
2. _____ indicates how far the data value is from the mean.
3. _____ is the absolute value of each deviation.
4. _____ is the average, or mean, of the absolute deviations.

Remember

To calculate the mean absolute deviation:

- Determine the mean of the data.
- Subtract the mean from each data value. These are the deviations.
- Record the absolute value of each deviation. These are the absolute deviations.
- Determine the mean of the absolute deviations. This is the mean absolute deviation.

Practice

Calculate the mean absolute deviation for each data set.

1. Data set: 4, 5, 9, 4, 8; Mean = 6
2. Data set: 7, 11, 8, 35, 14; Mean = 15
3. Data set: 60, 65, 66, 67, 67, 65; Mean = 65
4. Data set: 22, 26, 29, 23, 26, 21, 28, 24, 25, 26; Mean = 25
5. Data set: 180, 210, 155, 110, 230, 90, 400, 35, 190, 0, 10, 100, 90, 130, 200; Mean = 142
6. Data set: 55, 74, 90, 20, 47, 59, 26, 83, 77, 62, 58, 33, 57, 44, 31; Mean = 54.4

Stretch

1. Create a data set of 5 numbers that has a mean absolute deviation of 1.
   Explain how you arrived at your solution.
2. Create a data set of 6 numbers that has a mean absolute deviation of 10.
   Explain how you arrived at your solution.

Review

1. The rate at which crickets chirp is affected by the temperature. In fact, you can estimate the outside temperature by counting cricket chirps. As a homework assignment, Mr. Ortega asks each of his students to count the number of chirps they hear in 15 seconds at 8:00 pm. The results are shown.

   36, 37, 41, 39, 35, 39, 35, 39, 42, 37, 40, 35, 36, 37, 42, 35, 37, 37, 38, 42, 41, 37, 41

   Determine the median and mean number of cricket chirps heard in 15 seconds.

2. Patrick recorded the number of emails he sent over two weeks: 11, 5, 6, 9, 10, 5, 4, 2, 9, 10. What is the median of his data?

3. Order the integers in each group from least to greatest.
   a. 0, 115, −35, 32, −116, 92
   b. −2, 31, −5, 27, 0, 90

4. Determine each difference.
   a. $2\frac{4}{5} - 1\frac{1}{2}$
   b. $3 - 1\frac{1}{3}$

You Chose . . . Wisely

4

Choosing Appropriate Measures

WARM UP

Determine each measure for the data given in the stem-and-leaf plot.

Tweets Per Day

0	2 3 6 6 7
1	0 0 1 5
2	0
3	
4	
5	

Key: 2|0 = 20

1. mean

2. median

3. mean absolute deviation

LEARNING GOALS

- Determine whether the mean or median most appropriately represents a typical value in a data set.
- Understand how the distribution of a data set affects the different measures of central tendency and relate the choice of measures of center and variability to the context.
- Determine when to use the interquartile range and the mean absolute deviation to describe the variation of a data set.

You have learned about different measures of center and different measures of variation. Which of these measures are appropriate to use for data with different characteristics?

Nothing Changes, Nothing Stays the Same

1. Calculate the median and the mean of each data set.

   a. 10   20   30   40   50

   b. 10   20   25   35   40   50

   c. 10   20   30   40   500

2. Create a box-and-whisker plot for each data set.

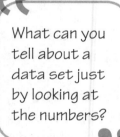

What can you tell about a data set just by looking at the numbers?

3. What patterns in the medians and means do you notice?

ACTIVITY
4.1

Choosing Median or Mean

The dot plot shows the amount of time Ben's friends spend exercising on weekdays.

Time Spent Exercising Each Weekday

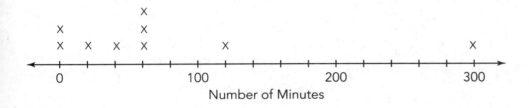

Number of Minutes

1. Ben says, "The mean will be greater than the median in this data set." Do you agree with Ben's statement?
   Explain your reasoning.

2. Determine the median and mean for the exercise data set.
   Explain how you determined each.

3. Would the mean or the median be the better measure to describe a typical value in the exercise data?
   Explain your reasoning.

4. The stem-and-leaf plot shown displays the scores of students on a 100-point math test.

Student Scores on a 100-Point Test

5	6 8
6	0 1
7	0 0 1 6 9
8	1 2 2 5 6 7 7 7 8 9
9	0 1 3 4 5 6

Key: 7|1 = 71 points

a. How many students are represented in the data?

b. Describe the shape of the distribution of the data.

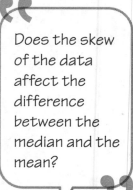

Does the skew of the data affect the difference between the median and the mean?

c. Do you think the mean test score is greater than, less than, or about the same as the median score? Explain.

d. Determine the median and mean. Identify which measure better represents a typical value in the data. Explain your reasoning.

5. The histogram shown displays the number of hours students spend playing video games each week.

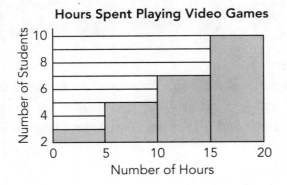

Hours Spent Playing Video Games

(y-axis: Number of Students, 2 to 10; x-axis: Number of Hours, 0 to 20)

a. How many students are represented in the data?

b. Describe the shape of the distribution of the data.

c. Identify which measure—median or mean—would better represent a typical value in the data. Explain your reasoning.

ACTIVITY 4.2

Mean or Median: Which Is Greater?

You have learned about three common distributions of data: skewed left, skewed right, and symmetric. You have also learned that the distribution of data can affect the measures of center.

Study the diagrams.

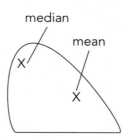

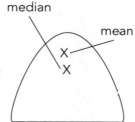

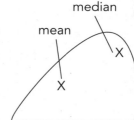

skewed right	**symmetric**	**skewed left**
The mean of a data set is greater than the median when the data is skewed to the right.	The mean and median are equal when the data is symmetric.	The mean of a data set is less than the median when the data is skewed to the left.
The median is the best measure of center because the median is not affected by very large data values.		The median is the best measure of center because the median is not affected by very small data values.

The median is not affected by very large or very small data values, but the mean is affected by these large and small values.

1. For each plot shown, first describe the distribution of data. Then, determine whether the mean is less than, greater than, or about equal to the median.

a.
Height of students in Room 201

```
5 | 4 6 6 8 8 9
6 | 0 0 1 2 3 3 4 5 6 6 6 8 8 9 9
7 | 0 0 1 1 1
```

Key: 6|3 = 63 inches

b.
Number of text messages sent by 6th graders

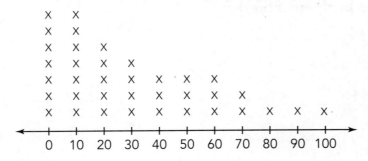

c.

Rock-Climbing Times of 6th-Grade Students

2. For each part in Question 1, determine whether the median or mean should be used to describe the center of the data.

Participation Number	Gold Medals Won
001	6
002	14
003	1
004	6
005	0
006	0
007	9
008	1
009	1
010	9
011	5
012	10
013	1
014	2
015	2
016	5
017	4
018	3

When a participant takes part in the Special Olympics, they receive a number. The table represents the first 18 people labeled by their participation number and the number of gold medals each participant won.

1. Analyze the data. Calculate the mean and mean absolute deviation, and then interpret the meaning of each in terms of the problem situation.

2. Construct a box-and-whisker plot of the data. Then determine and interpret the IQR.

3. Shelly says that the median and mean absolute deviation should be used to describe the data because the mean absolute deviation is less than the interquartile range. Is Shelly correct? Explain why or why not.

4. Which measure of central tendency and measure of variation should you use to describe the data? Explain your reasoning.

5. What conclusions can you draw about the number of gold medals participants won?

Data were collected from two airlines measuring the difference
in the stated departure times and the times the flights actually
departed. The average departure time differences were recorded
for each month for one year. The results are shown in the two
stem-and-leaf plots.

Difference in Departure Times (minutes)

My Air Airlines		Fly High Airlines	
Stem	Leaf	Stem	Leaf
0	0 5	0	7 8
1	1 5 9	1	4 5 6
2	0 0 6	2	4 7 9
3	3 3 4	3	0 2
4	0	4	5 9

$1|5 = 15$ minutes $2|4 = 24$ minutes

1. Describe the distribution of each data set.

Oh, I remember stem-and-leaf plots! There should be a key somewhere which shows how to read the data.

2. Determine an appropriate measure of central tendency and measure of variation for each data set. Then calculate each measure.

3. What conclusions can you draw from the measure of central tendency and measure of variation you chose?

4. You are scheduling a flight for an important meeting and you must be there on time. Which airline would you schedule with? Explain your reasoning.

TALK the TALK

All Together Now!

For each data set, calculate the median, mean, IQR, and MAD, if possible. Explain which measure of center and which measure of variation best describe the data set.

1.

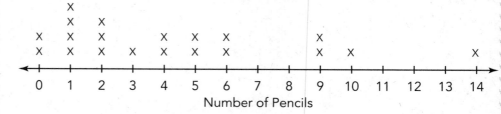

Pencils in Backpacks

Number of Pencils

2. **Ages of U.S. First Ladies (20th Century)**

3	1
4	0 3 4 5 7 8 9
5	0 2 4 6 6 6 9
6	0 0 3

Key: 6|0 means 60.

3. Prepare a presentation of your analysis of the data from Question 2 to give to the class.

Assignment

Write

In your own words, describe how you would decide whether to use the median or mean to represent the center of a data set.

Remember

When a data set is skewed right, the mean will be greater than the median. When a data set is skewed left, the mean will be less than the median. When a data set is symmetric, the mean and median will be approximately equal.

Practice

Branson Creek Middle School has decided to make fitness a key message to their students in the upcoming school year. As a result, they will be participating in a national fitness program. To participate, they must randomly select 15 students in the 5th grade and record their exercise time each day. The data (in minutes) are shown.

85, 80, 76, 78, 82, 88, 80, 80, 110, 85, 85, 82, 83, 88, 76

1. Construct a dot plot of the data.
2. Describe the distribution of the data.
3. Determine the median and mean of the data. Explain which measure better represents a typical value in the data set.
4. Determine which measure of variation to use to describe the spread of the data. Then calculate this measure.
5. Interpret the measure of variation you calculated.

Stretch

Cecile is applying for a job. She says that it must be a great place to work because it has a really high average salary. Explain to Cecile why this average might be misleading. Provide an example set of data to justify your argument.

Review

1. Complete each table to determine the mean absolute deviation.

a.

Data	Mean	Deviation From the Mean	Absolute Value of the Deviation From the Mean
35			
18			
58			
65			
29			
Mean Absolute Deviation			

b.

Data	Mean	Deviation From the Mean	Absolute Value of the Deviation From the Mean
19			
26			
45			
73			
27			
Mean Absolute Deviation			

2. Write the coordinates of each point described. Identify the quadrant in which the point is located.
   a. This point is a reflection across the y-axis of the point at (7, 1.5).
   b. This point is a reflection across the x-axis of the point at (3, 9).

3. Determine each quotient.
   a. $\frac{3}{5} \div \frac{4}{5}$
   b. $\frac{7}{8} \div 1\frac{1}{2}$

Numerical Summaries of Data Summary

KEY TERMS

- measure of center
- mode
- median
- balance point
- mean

- measures of variation
- range
- quartile
- interquartile range (IQR)
- box-and-whisker plot

- deviation
- absolute deviation
- mean absolute deviation

LESSON 1

In the Middle

When you analyze a set of data, you often want to describe it numerically. One way to numerically describe a data set is to use a measure of center. A **measure of center** tells you how the data values are clustered, or where the center of a graph of the data is located. There are three measures that describe how a data set is centered: the mean, the median, and the mode.

The **mode** is the data value or values that occur most frequently in a data set. A data set can have more than one mode or no mode. For example, the mode of the data set 12, 6, 12, 26, 4, and 12 is 12.

The **median** is the middle number in a data set when the values are placed in order from least to greatest or greatest to least. When a data set has an odd number of data values, you can determine which number is exactly in the middle of the data set. If there is an even number of data values, then the median is calculated by adding the two middle numbers and dividing by 2.

For example, the median of the data set 15, 12, 13, 10, 8, and 14 is 12.5.

The third measure of center is based on leveling off or creating fair shares. For example, if you had a stack of two cubes and a stack of six cubes, you can rearrange the stacks to create two equal stacks of four cubes each.

You can also represent quantities on a number line and create a balance point. When you have all the points at the same value, the number line is balanced. The value where the number line is balanced is called the **balance point**.

For example, consider the data set 2, 6.

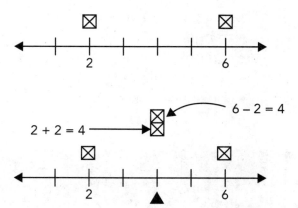

$$2 + 2 = 4$$

$$6 - 2 = 4$$

The value 2 was moved to the right from 2 to 4. To maintain balance, 6 was moved to the left from 6 to 4. The balance point is 4. The balance point can also be called the mean. The **mean** is the arithmetic average of the numbers in a data set.

For example, determine the mean of the data set: 12, 12, 6, 26, 4, 12.

The mean is calculated by adding all the values in the data set and dividing the sum by the number of values.

Step 1: $12 + 12 + 6 + 26 + 4 + 12 = 72$

Step 2: $\frac{72}{6} = 12$

You can verify that the mean is 12 because the balance point of the data set is 12.

A **measure of variation** describes the spread of data values. One measure of variation is the range. The **range** is the difference between the maximum and minimum values of a data set.

For example, the range of the data 200, 150, 260, 180, 300, 240, and 280 is 300 − 150 = 150.

Another set of values that helps to describe variation in a data set is a **quartile**. When data in a set are arranged in order, quartiles are the numbers that split data into quarters (or fourths). Quartiles are often denoted by the letter Q followed by a number that indicates which fourth it represents. Since the median is the second quartile, it could be denoted Q2. The other quartiles are Q1 and Q3. The **interquartile range**, abbreviated IQR, is the difference between the third quartile, Q3, and the first quartile, Q1. The IQR indicates the range of the middle 50 percent of the data.

To summarize and describe the spread of the data values, you can use the five-number summary. The five-number summary includes these 5 values from a data set:

- Minimum: the least value in the data set
- Q1: the first quartile
- Median: the median of the data set
- Q3: the third quartile
- Maximum: the greatest value in a data set.

For the data set 24, 32, 16, 18, 30, and 20, the minimum is 16, Q1 is 18, the median is 22, Q3 is 30, and the maximum is 32.

A **box-and-whisker plot**, or just box plot, is a graph that displays the five-number summary of a data set.

Parts of a Box-and-Whisker Plot

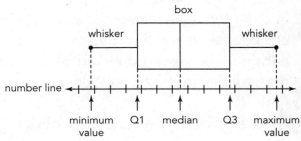

Box-and-whisker plots can be represented vertically as well as horizontally.

For example, in this box-and-whisker plot, the minimum of the data set is 15, Q1 is 40, the median of the data set is 56, Q3 is 70, and the maximum of the data set is 90.

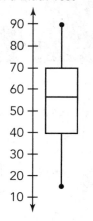

Number of Points Scored on a Math Test

March MADness

Another measure of variation that describes the spread of data values is **deviation**. The deviation of a data value indicates how far that data value is from the mean. To calculate the deviation, subtract the mean from the data value:

$$\text{Deviation} = \text{data value} - \text{mean}$$

For example, the mean of the data set 15, 12, 13, 10, 9, and 13 is 12.

The table describes each data point's deviation from the mean.

Data Point	15	12	13	10	9	13
Deviation from the Mean	3	0	1	−2	−3	1

In order to get an idea of the spread of the data values, you can take the absolute value of each deviation and then determine the mean of those absolute values. The absolute value of each deviation is called the **absolute deviation**. The **mean absolute deviation** (MAD) is the mean of the absolute deviations.

For example, the mean absolute deviation of the data shown in the table is

$$\frac{|3| + |0| + |1| + |-2| + |-3| + |1|}{6} = \frac{10}{6}.$$

So, the MAD is about 1.67.

The distribution of data can affect the measures of center.

The median is not affected by very large or very small data values, but the mean is affected by these large and small values. Therefore, the median is the best measure of center when the data is skewed left or right.

For example, the dot plot shows the amount of time Ben's friends spend exercising on weekdays.

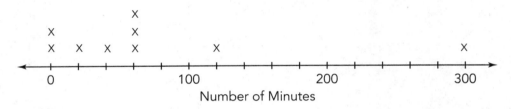

Time Spent Exercising Each Weekday

Number of Minutes

The data is skewed right, so the mean is greater than the median. The median for the data set is 60 minutes and the mean is 73.33 minutes. The median is a better measure to describe a typical value in the data.

The measure of central tendency and measure of variation used to best describe a data set depends on the values in the data set and the spread of those values. If you use the median to describe the measure of center, you should use the IQR to describe the measure of variation, and if you use the mean to describe the measure of center, you should use the mean absolute deviation to describe the measure of variation.

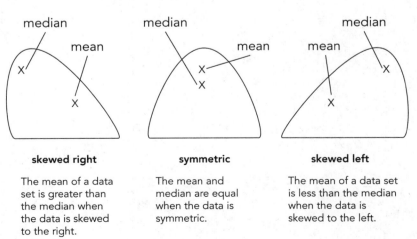

skewed right

The mean of a data set is greater than the median when the data is skewed to the right.

symmetric

The mean and median are equal when the data is symmetric.

skewed left

The mean of a data set is less than the median when the data is skewed to the left.

Glossary

---A---

absolute deviation

The absolute value of each deviation is called the absolute deviation.

Example

$$11 - 12 = -1$$

data　mean　deviaton

$$|-1| = 1$$

deviation　absolute
deviation

---

absolute value

The absolute value, or magnitude, of a number is its distance from zero on a number line.

Example

The absolute value of −3 is the same as the absolute value of 3 because they are both a distance of 3 from zero on a number line.

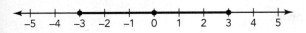

$$|-3| = |3|$$

Addition Property of Equality

The Addition Property of Equality states that if two values a and b are equal, when you add the same value c to each, the sums are equal.

Examples

$12 = 12$ and $12 + 7 = 12 + 7$

If $a = b$, then $a + c = b + c$.

---

additive reasoning

Additive reasoning focuses on the use of addition and subtraction for comparisons.

Example

Vicki is 40 years old and Ben is 10 years old. In 5 years, Vicki will be 45 and Ben will be 15. Vicki will always be 30 years older than Ben. This is additive reasoning.

---

algebraic expression

An algebraic expression is a mathematical phrase that has at least one variable, and it can contain numbers and operation symbols.

Examples

a　　$2a + b$　　xy　　$\dfrac{4}{P}$　　z^2

---

altitude

The altitude of a figure is the perpendicular distance from a vertex to the line containing the opposite side, represented by a line segment.

Examples

altitude of a
parallelogram

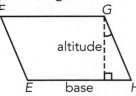

altitude of
a triangle

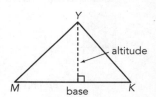

altitude of a trapezoid

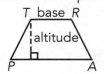

balance point

When you have all the points on a number line at the same value, the number line is balanced. The value where the number line is balanced is called the balance point.

Example

Consider the data set: 2, 6.

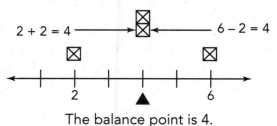

$2 + 2 = 4$ $6 - 2 = 4$

The balance point is 4.

bar graph

A bar graph displays categorical data using either horizontal or vertical bars on a graph. The height or length of each bar indicates the value for that category.

Examples

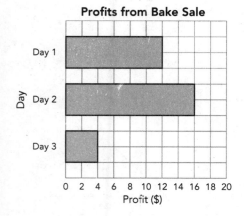

bar model

A bar model uses rectangular bars to represent known and unknown quantities.

Example

You can use a bar model to solve the equation $x + 10 = 15$.

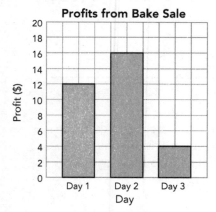

The top bar can be split into two bars, x and 10. When this split happens in the bottom bar, with one bar containing 10, it shows that x is the same as 5, so $x = 5$.

base

The base of a power is the factor that is multiplied repeatedly in the power.

Examples

$$2^3 = 2 \times 2 \times 2 = 8 \qquad 8^0 = 1$$

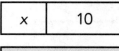

base   base

benchmark fractions

Benchmark fractions are common fractions you can use to estimate the value of fractions.

Example

The numbers 0, $\frac{1}{2}$, and 1 are some benchmark fractions.

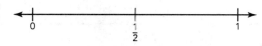

benchmark percents

A benchmark percent is a percent that is commonly used, such as 1%, 5%, 10%, 25%, 50%, and 100%.

box-and-whisker plot

A box-and-whisker plot, or just box plot, is a graph that displays the five-number summary of a data set: the median, the upper and lower quartiles (Q1 and Q3), and the minimum and maximum values.

Example

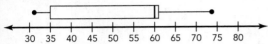

30 35 40 45 50 55 60 65 70 75 80

Data: 32, 35, 35, 53, 55, 60, 60, 61, 61, 74, 74

Minimum = 32

Q1 = 35

Median = 60

Q3 = 61

Maximum = 74

—————— C ——————

categorical data

Categorical data, or qualitative data, are data for which each piece of data fits into exactly one of several different groups or categories.

Examples

Animals: lions, tigers, bears, etc.

Colors: blue, green, red, etc.

circle graph

A circle graph, often called a pie chart, displays categorical data using sectors, or "wedges," of a circle.

Example

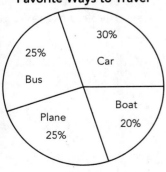

Favorite Ways to Travel

25% Bus
30% Car
20% Boat
25% Plane

clusters

Clusters are areas of the graph where data are grouped close together.

Example

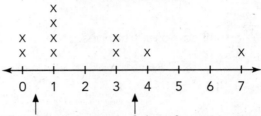

Number of Pets

0 1 2 3 4 5 6 7

There are clusters of data from 0 to 1 and from 3 to 4.

coefficient

A number that is multiplied by a variable in an algebraic expression is called a coefficient.

Examples

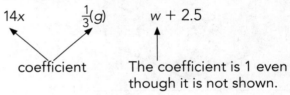

$14x$ $\frac{1}{3}(g)$ $w + 2.5$

coefficient   The coefficient is 1 even though it is not shown.

common factor

A common factor is a number that is a factor of two or more numbers.

Example

factors of 60: **1**, **2**, **3**, **4**, 5, **6**, 10, **12**, 15, 20, 30, 60

factors of 24: 1, **2**, **3**, **4**, **6**, 8, **12**, 24

common factors of 60 and 24: 1, 2, 3, 4, 6, and 12

Commutative Property of Multiplication

The Commutative Property of Multiplication states that for any numbers a and b, the product $a \cdot b$ is equal to the product $b \cdot a$.

Examples

$$\begin{array}{r} 29 \\ \times 3 \\ \hline 87 \end{array} = \begin{array}{r} 3 \\ \times 29 \\ \hline 27 \\ + 60 \\ \hline 87 \end{array}$$

$$\frac{1}{5} \times \frac{2}{3} = \frac{2}{3} \times \frac{1}{5}$$
$$\frac{2}{15} \qquad \frac{2}{15}$$

complex fraction

A complex fraction is a fraction that has a fraction in either the numerator, the denominator, or both the numerator and denominator.

Examples

$\frac{\frac{3}{4}}{3}, \frac{\frac{7}{1}}{2}$, and $\frac{\frac{1}{4}}{\frac{2}{3}}$ are all complex fractions.

composite solid

A composite solid is made up of more than one geometric solid.

Example

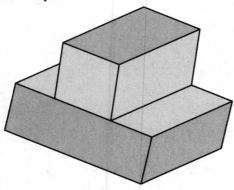

continuous graph

A continuous graph is a graph with no breaks in it.

Examples

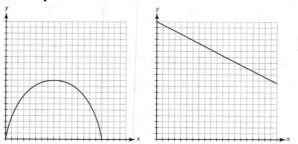

convert

To convert a measurement means to change it to an equivalent measurement in different units.

Example

To convert 36 inches to feet, you can multiply:

$36 \text{ in.} \left(\frac{1 \text{ ft}}{12 \text{ in.}} \right) = \frac{36 \text{ ft}}{12}$

$= 3 \text{ft}$

cube

A cube is a polyhedron that has congruent squares as faces.

Example

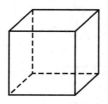

─────────── D ───────────

data

Data are categories, numbers, or observations gathered in response to a statistical question.

Examples

favorite foods of sixth graders,
heights of different animals at the zoo

Density Property

The Density Property states that between any two rational numbers there is another rational number.

dependent quantity

The dependent quantity is the quantity that depends on another in a problem situation.

Example

Max just got a new hybrid car that averages 51 miles to the gallon. How far does the car travel on 15 gallons of fuel?

number of gallons $\cdot \frac{\text{miles}}{\text{gallon}} =$ miles traveled

The dependent quantity is the total miles traveled. The number of miles traveled depends on the gallons of fuel.

dependent variable

The variable that represents the dependent quantity is called the dependent variable.

Example

Max just got a new hybrid car that averages 51 miles to the gallon. How far does the car travel on 15 gallons of fuel?

number of gallons $\cdot \frac{\text{miles}}{\text{gallon}}$ = miles traveled

$$g \cdot m = t$$

The dependent quantity is the total miles traveled. Since t represents total miles traveled in the equation, t is the dependent variable.

deviation

The deviation of a data value indicates how far that data value is from the mean.

Example

deviation = data value − mean

discrete graph

A discrete graph is a graph of isolated points.

Examples

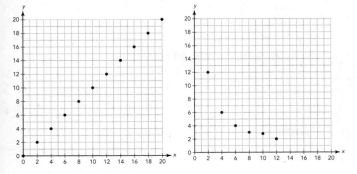

distribution

The overall shape of a graph is called the distribution of data. A distribution is the way in which the data are spread out.

Distributive Property

The Distributive Property states that for any numbers a, b, and c, $a(b + c) = ab + ac$.

Examples

$$4(2 + 15) = 4 \cdot 2 + 4 \cdot 15$$
$$= 8 + 60$$
$$= 68$$

Division Property of Equality

The Division Property of Equality states that when you divide equal values a and b by the same value c and $c \neq 0$, the quotients are equal.

Examples

$12 = 12$ and $12 \div 7 = 12 \div 7$

If $a = b$ and $c \neq 0$, then $\frac{a}{c} = \frac{b}{c}$.

dot plot

A dot plot (sometimes called a line plot) is a data display that shows discrete data on a number line with dots, Xs, or other symbols.

Example

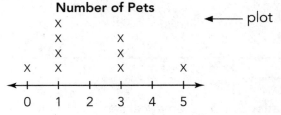

double number line

A double number line is a model that is made up of two number lines used together to represent the ratio between two quantities.

Example

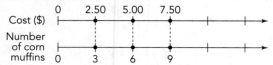

E

---

edge

An edge is the intersection of two faces of a three-dimensional figure.

Example

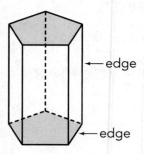

---

ellipsis

An ellipsis is a set of three periods used to represent infinity in a number set.

Example

$$\{..., -2, -1, 0, 1, 2, ...\}$$
$$\uparrow \qquad\qquad\qquad \uparrow$$
$$\text{ellipsis} \qquad\qquad \text{ellipsis}$$

---

equation

An equation is a mathematical sentence that uses an equals sign to show that two quantities are the same as one another.

Examples

$$y = 2x + 4$$
$$6 = 3 + 3$$
$$2(8) = 26 - 10$$
$$\frac{1}{4} \cdot 4 = \frac{8}{4} - \frac{4}{4}$$

---

equivalent expressions

Two algebraic expressions are equivalent expressions if, when any values are substituted for variables, the results are equal.

Example

$$(x + 10) + (6x - 5) = 7x + 5$$
$$12 + 7 = 14 + 5$$
$$19 = 19$$

---

equivalent ratios

Equivalent ratios are ratios that represent the same part-to-part or part-to-whole relationship.

---

evaluate an algebraic expression

To evaluate an algebraic expression means to determine the value of the expression for a given value of each variable.

Example

Evaluate the expression $\dfrac{4x + (2^3 - y)}{p}$ for $x = 2.5$, $y = 8$, and $p = 2$.

- First replace the variables with numbers: $\dfrac{4(2.5) + (2^3 - 8)}{2}$
- Then calculate the value of the expression: $\dfrac{10 + 0}{2} = \dfrac{10}{2} = 5$.

---

evaluate a numeric expression

To evaluate a numeric expression means to simplify the expression to a single numeric value.

Example

$$19 - 4 \times 3$$
$$19 - 12$$
$$7$$

experiment

An experiment is one method of collecting data in which a researcher imposes a condition and observes the results.

Example

A researcher conducts an experiment to investigate if 6th graders perform better on an assessment if they read a textbook or watch a video about the material. The researcher randomly assigns half the students to read the text and half the students to watch the video. All students would be given the same assessment and the scores of the students in the two groups would be compared.

exponent

The exponent of the power is the number of times the base is used as a factor.

Examples

$2^3 = 2 \times 2 \times 2$

↑
exponent

$8^4 = 8 \times 8 \times 8 \times 8$

↑
exponent

--- F ---

face

A face is one of the polygons that makes up a polyhedron.

Example

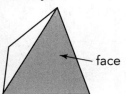

face

frequency

A frequency is the number of times an item or number occurs in a data set.

Example

Number Rolled	Tally	Frequency
2									7

The number 2 was rolled 7 times, so its frequency was 7.

--- G ---

gaps

Gaps are areas of the graph where there are no data.

Example

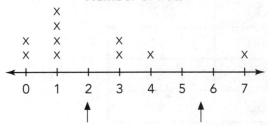

There are gaps between 1 and 3 and between 4 and 7.

geometric solid

A geometric solid is a bounded three-dimensional geometric figure.

Example

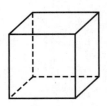

graph of an inequality

The graph of an inequality in one variable is the set of all points on a number line that make the inequality true.

Example

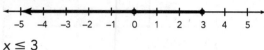

$x \le 3$

grouped frequency table

A grouped frequency table is a table used to organize data according to how many times data values with a given range of values occur.

Example

Floor Intervals	Frequency (f)
10–20	8
20–30	27
30–40	16
40–50	5
50–60	4

greatest common factor (GCF)

The greatest common factor, or GCF, is the largest factor two or more numbers have in common.

Example

factors of 16: **1**, **2**, **4**, 8, 16

factors of 12: **1**, **2**, 3, **4**, 6, 12

common factors: 1, 2, 4

greatest common factor: 4

H
---

histogram

A histogram is a graphical way to display quantitative or numerical data using vertical bars. The width of a bar represents an interval of data and is often referred to as a bin. The height of the bar indicates the frequency, or the number of data values included in any given bin.

Example

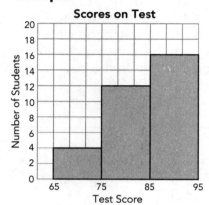

I

Identity Property of Addition

The Identity Property of Addition states that the sum of any number and 0 is the number.

Examples

$6 \times 0 = 6$ $\qquad$ $\frac{3}{4} + 0 = \frac{3}{4}$

$5^2 + 0 = 5^2$ $\qquad$ $0.125 + 0 = 0.125$

Identity Property of Multiplication

The Identity Property of Multiplication states that the product of any number and 1 is the number.

Examples

$6 \times 1 = 6$ $\qquad$ $\frac{3}{4} \times 1 = \frac{3}{4}$

$5^2 \cdot 1 = 5^2$ $\qquad$ $0.125(1) = 0.125$

independent quantity

The independent quantity is the quantity the dependent quantity depends on.

Example

Max just got a new hybrid car that averages 51 miles to the gallon. How far does the car travel on 15 gallons of fuel?

number of gallons $\cdot \dfrac{\text{miles}}{\text{gallon}} =$ miles traveled

The independent quantity is the number of gallons. The other quantity (miles traveled) is dependent upon this quantity.

independent variable

The variable that represents the independent quantity is called the independent variable.

Example

Max just got a new hybrid car that averages 51 miles to the gallon. How far does the car travel on 15 gallons of fuel?

number of gallons $\cdot \dfrac{\text{miles}}{\text{gallon}} =$ miles traveled

$$g \cdot m = t$$

The independent quantity is the number of gallons. Since g represents the number of gallons in the equation, g is the independent variable.

infinity

Infinity, represented by the symbol ∞, means a quantity with no end or bound.

Example

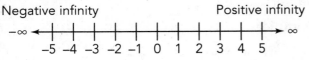

Negative infinity   Positive infinity

integers

Integers are the set of whole numbers with their opposites.

Example

The set of integers can be represented as $\{\ldots -3, -2, -1, 0, 1, 2, 3, \ldots\}$

interquartile range (IQR)

The interquartile range, abbreviated IQR, is the difference between the third quartile, Q3, and the first quartile, Q1. The IQR indicates the range of the middle 50 percent of the data.

Example

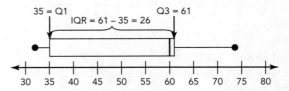

inverse operations

Inverse operations are pairs of operations that reverse the effects of each other.

Examples

Addition and subtraction are inverse operations: $351 + 25 - 25 = 351$.

Multiplication and division are inverse operations: $351 \times 25 \div 25 = 351$.

K

kite

A kite is a quadrilateral with two pairs of consecutive congruent sides where opposite sides are not congruent.

Example

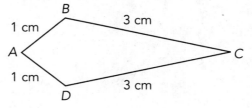

L

least common multiple (LCM)

The least common multiple, or LCM, is the smallest multiple (other than zero) that two or more numbers have in common.

Example

multiples of 60: 60, **120**, 180, **240**, 300, 360, 420, 480 . . .

multiples of 24: 24, 48, 72, 96, **120**, 144, 168, 192, 216, **240** . . .

some common multiples of 60 and 24: 120, 240 . . .

least common multiple of 60 and 24: 120

like terms

In an algebraic expression, like terms are two or more terms that have the same variable raised to the same power.

Examples

like terms

$$4x + 3p + x + 2 = 5x + 3p + 2$$

like terms

$$24a^2 + 2a - 9a^2 = 13a^2 + 2a$$

no like terms
$$m + m^2 - x + x^3$$

line segment

A line segment is a portion of a line that includes two points and all the points between those two points.

Example

Line segment *AB* is shown.

linear relationship

When a set of points graphed on a coordinate plane forms a straight line, a linear relationship exists.

Example

The points graphed show a linear relationship.

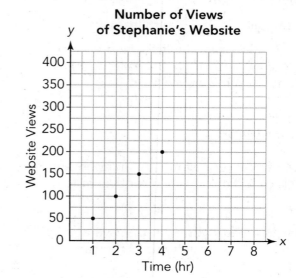

literal equation

A literal equation is an equation in which the variables represent specific measures.

Examples

$$A = lw \qquad A = \frac{1}{2} bh \qquad d = rt$$

M

mean

The mean is the arithmetic average of the numbers in a data set.

Example

Number of Pets

```
              X
              X
     X        X            X
     X        X            X            X
  ◄──┼────┼────┼────┼────┼────┼──►
     0    1    2    3    4    5
```

Mean $= \dfrac{0 + 0 + 1 + 1 + 1 + 1 + 3 + 3 + 5}{9}$

$= \dfrac{15}{9} = 1\frac{2}{3}$ pets

mean absolute deviation

The mean absolute deviation is the average or mean of the absolute deviations.

measure of center

A measure of center tells you how the data values are clustered, or where the "center" of a graph of the data is located.

Examples

Mean, median, and mode are each a measure of center for data.

measure of variation

A measure of variation describes the spread of data values.

Example

Range is a measure of variation for data.

median

The median is the middle number in a data set when the values are placed in order from least to greatest or greatest to least.

Example

Number of Pets

X
X
X   X   X
X   X   X   X
```
←+---+---+---+---+---+→
  0   1   2   3   4   5
```
0, 0, 1, 1, 1, 1, 3, 3, 5

↑
median

mode

The mode is the value or values that occur most frequently in a data set.

Example

Number of Pets

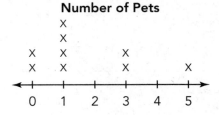

0, 0, 1, 1, 1, 1, 3, 3, 5

The mode of the data is 1.

multiple

A multiple is the product of a given whole number and another whole number.

Example

multiples of 10:

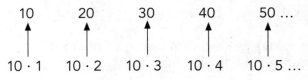

Multiplication Property of Equality

The Multiplication Property of Equality states that if two values a and b are equal, when you multiply each by the same value c, the products are equal.

Examples

$12 = 12$ and $12(7) = 12(7)$

If $a = b$, then $ac = bc$.

multiplicative inverse

The multiplicative inverse of a number $\frac{a}{b}$ is the number $\frac{b}{a}$, where a and b are nonzero numbers. The product of any nonzero number and its multiplicative inverse is 1.

Examples

The multiplicative inverse of $\frac{3}{7}$ is $\frac{7}{3}$: $\frac{3}{7} \times \frac{7}{3} = \frac{21}{21} = 1$

The multiplicative inverse of 5 is $\frac{1}{5}$: $\frac{5}{1} \times \frac{1}{5} = \frac{5}{5} = 1$

Multiplicative Inverse Property

The Multiplicative Inverse Property states:
$\frac{a}{b} \cdot \frac{b}{a} = 1$, where a and b are nonzero numbers.

Examples

$\frac{3}{7} \times \frac{7}{3} = \frac{21}{21} = 1$

$\frac{5}{1} \times \frac{1}{5} = \frac{5}{5} = 1$

multiplicative reasoning

Multiplicative reasoning focuses on the use of multiplication and division.

Example

Vicki is 40 years old and Ben is 10 years old. Vicki is 4 times as old as Ben. In 5 years, Vicki will be 3 times as old as Ben.

This is multiplicative reasoning.

— N —

negative numbers

The values to the left of zero on a number line are called negative numbers.

Example

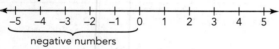

net

A net is a two-dimensional representation of a three-dimensional geometric figure.

Example

A net of a cube is shown.

numeric expression

A numeric expression is a mathematical phrase that contains numbers and operations.

Example

$5 \times 4 - 9$

— O —

observational study

An observational study is one method of collecting data in which a researcher collects data by observing the variable of interest.

Example

A researcher is interested in whether or not more men or women prefer a certain store. The researcher observes the number of men and women who visit the store over a number of hours and compares the values of the two groups.

one-step equation

A one-step equation is an equation that can be solved using only one operation.

Order of Operations

The Order of Operations is a set of rules that ensures the same result every time an expression is evaluated.

Example

$44 + (6 - 5) - 2 \times 75 \div 5^1$ Parentheses

$44 + 1 - 2 \times 75 \div 5^1$ Exponents

$44 + 1 - 2 \times 75 \div 5$ Multiplication and Division (from left to right)

$44 + 1 - 150 \div 5$

$44 + 1 - 30$ Addition and Subtraction (from left to right)

$45 - 30$

15

outliers

Outliers are data values that lie a large distance from the other data in a graph. Outliers usually accompany gaps in data.

Example

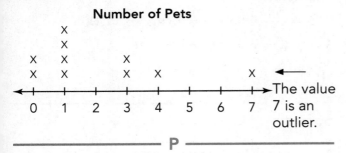

The value 7 is an outlier.

P

---

parallelogram

A parallelogram is a four-sided figure with two pairs of parallel sides and opposite sides that are equal in length.

Examples

In parallelogram *ABCD*, opposite sides *AB* and *CD* are parallel and equal in length; opposite sides *AD* and *BC* are parallel and equal in length.

In parallelogram *EFGH*, opposite sides *EF* and *GH* are parallel and equal in length; opposite sides *FG* and *EH* are parallel and equal in length.

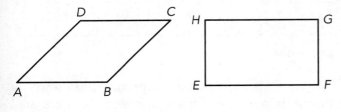

peaks

Peaks are values on a graph that contain more data points than the values on either side of it.

Example

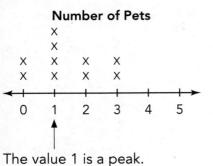

The value 1 is a peak.

percent

A percent is a part-to-whole ratio where the whole is equal to 100. Percent is another name for hundredths. The percent symbol "%" means "per 100," or "out of 100."

---

perfect cube

A perfect cube is the cube of a whole number.

Example

64 is a perfect cube: $4 \times 4 \times 4 = 64$

---

perfect square

A perfect square is the square of an integer.

Examples

9 is a perfect square: $3 \times 3 = 9$

25 is a perfect square: $5 \times 5 = 25$

---

point

A point is a location in space. A point has no size or shape, but it is often represented by using a dot and is named by a capital letter.

Examples

Points *A* and *B* are shown.

A•

    •B

polygon

A polygon is a closed figure formed by three or more line segments.

Examples

A trapezoid is a polygon.

A pentagon is a polygon.

A circle is NOT a polygon.

polyhedron

A polyhedron is a three-dimensional solid figure that has polygons as faces.

Example

A cube is a polyhedron. It has six square faces.

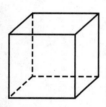

population

A population is an entire set of items from which data are collected.

Example

If you wanted to determine the average height of the students at your school, the number of students at the school would be the population.

positive rational number

A positive rational number is a number that can be written in the form $\frac{a}{b}$, where a and b are both whole numbers greater than 0.

Examples

$0.75 = \frac{75}{100}$, where $a = 75$ and $b = 100$

$6 = \frac{6}{1}$, where $a = 6$ and $b = 1$

$\frac{9}{11}$, where $a = 9$ and $b = 11$

power

A power has two elements: the base and the exponent.

Example

base $\longrightarrow$ $\underset{\text{power}}{6^2}$ $\longleftarrow$ exponent

proportion

A proportion is an equation that states that two ratios are equal.

Example

$\frac{1}{2} = \frac{4.5}{9}$

pyramid

A pyramid is a polyhedron with one base and the same number of triangular faces as there are sides of the base.

Example

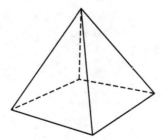

Q

quadrants

The x- and y-axes divide the coordinate plane into four regions called quadrants. These quadrants are numbered with Roman numerals from one (I) to four (IV), starting in the upper right-hand quadrant and moving counterclockwise.

Example

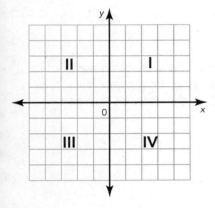

quantitative data

Quantitative data, or numerical data, are data for which each piece of data can be placed on a numerical scale and compared.

Examples

The zoo has 4 lions, 3 tigers, and 6 bears.

In 2006, Los Angeles had a population of about 3,849,378. In the same year, Atlanta had a population of about 429,500.

quartiles

Quartiles are a set of values that describe variation in a data set. When data in a set are arranged in order, quartiles are the numbers that split data into quarters (or fourths).

Example

first quartile (Q1)   third quartile (Q3)

Data: 32, 35, 35, 53, 55, 60, 60, 61, 61, 74, 74

second quartile/median (Q2)

R

range

The range is the difference between the maximum and minimum values of a data set.

Example

Number of Pets

```
        X
        X
X   X       X
X   X       X       X
+---+---+---+---+---+--->
0   1   2   3   4   5
```

0, 0, 1, 1, 1, 1, 3, 3, 5

$5 - 0 = 5$

The range of the data is 5.

rate

A rate is a ratio that compares two quantities that are measured in different units.

Example

The speed of 60 miles in two hours is a rate:

$$\frac{60 \text{ mi}}{2 \text{ h}} = \frac{30 \text{ mi}}{1 \text{ h}}$$

ratio

A ratio is a comparison of two quantities that uses division.

Examples

☆ ☆ ☆ ○ ○

The ratio of stars to circles is $\frac{3}{2}$, or 3:2, or 3 to 2.

The ratio of circles to stars is $\frac{2}{3}$, or 2:3, or 2 to 3.

rational numbers

Rational numbers are the set of numbers that can be written as $\frac{a}{b}$, where a and b are integers and $b \neq 0$.

Examples

-4, $\frac{1}{2}$, $\frac{2}{3}$, 0.67, and $\frac{22}{7}$ are examples of rational numbers.

reciprocal

The reciprocal of a number is also known as the multiplicative inverse of the number. (See *multiplicative inverse*.)

Examples

The reciprocal of $\frac{3}{7}$ is $\frac{7}{3}$: $\frac{3}{7} \times \frac{7}{3} = \frac{21}{21} = 1$

The reciprocal of 5 is $\frac{1}{5}$: $\frac{5}{1} \times \frac{1}{5} = \frac{5}{5} = 1$

Reflexive Property of Equality

The Reflexive Property of Equality says that when both sides of an equation look exactly the same, their values are equal.

Examples

$7 = 7$

$a = a$

relatively prime

Two numbers that do not have any common factors other than 1 are called relatively prime.

Examples

Positive whole number pairs that have a difference of 1 (4 and 5, 10 and 11, 15 and 16) are always relatively prime.

right rectangular prism

A right rectangular prism is a polyhedron with three pairs of congruent and parallel rectangular faces.

Example

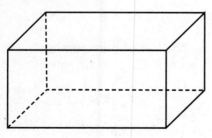

sample

A sample is a selection from a population.

Example

If you wanted to determine the average height of the students in your school, you could choose a certain number of students and measure their heights. The heights of the students in this group would be your sample.

scaling down

Scaling down means to divide both parts of the ratio by the same factor greater than 1, or multiply both parts of the ratio by the same factor less than 1.

Example

scaling up

Scaling up means to multiply both parts of a ratio by the same factor greater than 1.

Example

skewed left distribution

In a skewed left distribution of data the peak of the data is to the right side of the graph. There are only a few data points to the left side of the graph.

Example

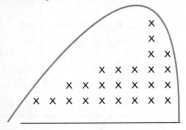

skewed right distribution

In a skewed right distribution of data the peak of the data is to the left side of the graph. There are only a few data points to the right side of the graph.

Example

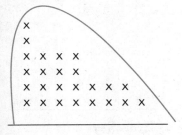

slant height

A slant height of a pyramid is the distance measured along a triangular face from the vertex of the pyramid to the midpoint, or center, of one of the edges of the base.

Example

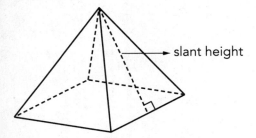

slant height

solution

A solution to an equation is any value for a variable that makes the equation true.

Example

The solution to the equation $2x + 4 = 8$ is $x = 2$.

solution set of an inequality

The set of all points that make an inequality true is the solution set of the inequality.

Examples

$x \geq 7$

The solution set for $x \geq 7$ is all the numbers greater than or equal to 7.

$x < 7$

The solution set for $x < 7$ is all the numbers less than 7.

statistical process

The statistical process has four components:
- Formulating a statistical question.
- Collecting appropriate data.
- Analyzing the data graphically and numerically.
- Interpreting the results of the analysis.

statistical question

A statistical question is a question that anticipates an answer based on data that vary.

Example

"What sport is the most popular in your school?" is a statistical question because it anticipates that the answers will vary since not everyone at your school is likely to have the same favorite sport.

"How many students are in Chess Club?" is NOT a statistical question because there is only one answer to the question.

stem-and-leaf plot

A stem-and-leaf plot is a graphical method used to represent ordered numerical data. Once the data are ordered, the stem and leaves are determined. Typically, the stem is all the digits in a number except the rightmost digit, which is the leaf.

Example

Books Read in Mr. Brown's Class

0	3, 6
1	0, 1, 5
2	
3	9, 9
4	0, 0, 0

Key: 1 | 0 = 10.

Subtraction Property of Equality

The Subtraction Property of Equality states that when you subtract the same value c from equal values a and b, the differences are equal.

Examples

$12 = 12$ and $12 - 7 = 12 - 7$

If $a = b$, then $a - c = b - c$.

surface area

The surface area of a polyhedron is the total area of all its two-dimensional faces.

Example

The surface area of a unit cube is 6 square units. The cube has 6 faces and the area of each face is 1 square unit.

survey

A survey is one method of collecting data in which people are asked one or more questions.

Example

A restaurant may ask its customers to complete a survey with the following question:

On a scale of 1–10, with 1 meaning "poor" and 10 meaning "excellent," how would you rate the food you ate?

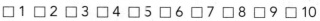

□ 1 □ 2 □ 3 □ 4 □ 5 □ 6 □ 7 □ 8 □ 9 □ 10

symmetric distribution

In a symmetric distribution of data the left and right halves of the graph are mirror images of each other. The peak is in the middle because there are many data values in the center.

Example

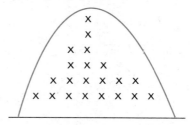

Symmetric Property of Equality

The Symmetric Property of Equality states that if $a = b$, then $b = a$.

Example

$x = 3$ is the same as $3 = x$.

T
---

tape diagram

A tape diagram illustrates number relationships by using rectangles to represent ratio parts.

Example

A bakery sells packs of muffins in the ratio of 3 blueberry muffins : 2 pumpkin muffins : 1 bran muffin. The tape diagram represents the ratio of each type of muffin.

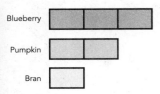

term

A term of an algebraic expression is a number, variable, or product of numbers and variables.

Example

The expression has four terms.

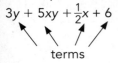

$$3y + 5xy + \frac{1}{2}x + 6$$

terms

trailing zeros

Trailing zeros are a sequence of 0s in a decimal representation of a number, after which no non-zero digits follow.

Example

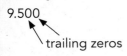

9.500

trailing zeros

trapezoid

A trapezoid is a quadrilateral with two bases that are parallel to each other, often labeled b_1 and b_2.

Example

Quadrilateral *ABCD* is a trapezoid. Side *BC* is parallel to side *AD*.

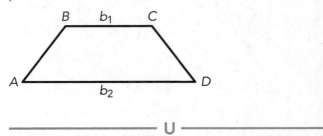

U
---

unit rate

A unit rate is a comparison of two different measurements in which the numerator or denominator has a value of one unit.

Example

The speed 60 miles in 2 hours can be written as a unit rate:

$$\frac{60 \text{ mi}}{2 \text{ h}} = \frac{30 \text{ mi}}{1 \text{ h}}.$$

The unit rate is 30 miles per hour.

V
---

variability

In statistics, variability means that the value of the attribute being studied can change from one person or thing to another.

variable

A variable is a letter or symbol that is used to represent a number.

Examples

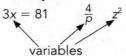

$$3x = 81 \qquad \frac{4}{p} \qquad z^2$$

variables

vertex

A vertex of a polyhedron is a point at which three or more of its edges meet.

Example

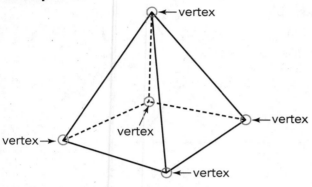

volume

Volume is the amount of space occupied by an object. Volume is measured in cubic units.

Zero Property of Multiplication

The Zero Property of Multiplication states that the product of any number and 0 is 0.

Examples

$6 \times 0 = 0$ $\qquad$ $\frac{3}{4} \times 0 = 0$

$5^2 \cdot 0 = 0$ $\qquad$ $0.125(0)\, 0 = 0$

Index